Roger Newman Turner practised for fifty-two years as a naturopath, osteopath, and acupuncturist in the clinics established by his father in Letchworth Garden City and London. He is the author of a number of books on diet and health and has lectured internationally on naturopathic medicine.

D1545834

For Jade and Caspian
Challenge orthodoxy and seek wisdom in Nature.

Roger Newman Turner

AGAINST THE GRAIN

The life of Frank
Newman Turner

AUSTIN MACAULEY PUBLISHERS™
LONDON • CAMBRIDGE • NEW YORK • SHARJAH

A CIP catalogue record for this title is available from the British Library.

ISBN 9781787108035 (Paperback)
ISBN 9781787108073 (ePub e-book)

www.austinmacauley.com

First Published 2022
Austin Macauley Publishers Ltd®
1 Canada Square
Canary Wharf
London
E14 5AA

4-8-2023 · *Start* 7:00 AM
Jmsh

Delving into the past, one relies a great deal on documentary evidence, both fragmentary and more orderly, for almost all who were acquainted with the subject are no longer alive. But there are still some with us whose recollections, however sketchy, have given valuable insights from their particular perspectives.

My brothers, Giles and Adam, have provided wise guidance throughout this project, bringing vignettes of family life, particularly of Frank's final years, when, as the eldest son, I was not often at home to experience them at first hand. Our cousins, Rowena Stewart, Susan Stenton, Catherine Farmer, and Jonathan Turner have all provided background on Frank's wider family and Yorkshire surroundings. Jonathan's extensive researches into our ancestry have been particularly informative.

Dr Bidisha Mallik, who has conducted meticulous research into the life of Mirabehn, a close associate of Mahatma Gandhi, has given valuable information about Mirabehn's correspondence with my father in her attempts to further Gandhi's ideas on environmental and social reform in North-West India. I am also grateful to Steve Engelking, the biographer of Hugh J Schonfield, who, with his wife Helene, were close friends of my parents in their early days at Goosegreen, for permission to quote from Hugh's writing.

The task of transcribing early drafts of this memoir to computer keyboard fell to Judie Starkey, who fitted this around her responsibilities as a loyal secretary and receptionist in our naturopathic clinical practice for over 25 years. I am indebted to Amy Neil McBride who applied her considerable editorial expertise to the improvement of my introduction and some of the early chapters. Our son, Julian, of Lucid Dream Pictures, gave helpful technical assistance with preparation of photographs.

Finally, to my wife, Birgid, and family, I can only apologise for living in the past for so many years whilst I endeavoured to construct this memoir. I hope that at least it will be a worthy record of our heritage.

Roger Newman Turner
Weymouth, Dorset. 2021

Introduction

As a boy on our family farm in Somerset I used to go into the dairy after milking time and scoop some cream off the top of the churn containing some of the day's milk from our Jersey cows. It was, of course, unpasteurised and nutritious and it is a good metaphor for the unorthodox environment in which I grew up. Although we may not have appreciated it at the time, my brothers and I were brought up by parents who went against the grain of conventional agriculture and defied many of the other orthodoxies that most people unquestioningly accept as normal. But the cream at the top was only a small part of the richness that lay beneath.

My father, Frank Newman Turner, the son of Yorkshire tenant farmers, seldom ploughed a conventional furrow. Faced with a rundown West Country farm and escalating veterinary bills for an ailing herd of cattle, he abandoned the conventions of his orthodox agricultural training, and inspired by his mentor, Sir Albert Howard set about restoring the health of his farm's soil and livestock by working with nature, rather than against it. It was through a deep respect for all living things, whether plant, animal, or human, that he became a vegetarian, conscientious objector, peace campaigner, and the author of several practical organic farming books, published by Faber and Faber. He founded, edited, and published one of the UK's first eco-agriculture magazines, *The Farmer*, and later, moving from animal to human health, became a medical herbalist and naturopath.

Sir Albert Howard, a giant of the organic movement, who insisted Frank must write his practical books

This much we knew from conversations around the family dinner table and childhoods that differed from those of our peers. It was the cream at the top of the churn, but we knew little of the struggles and sacrifices that such a life entailed. Fortunately, as it turned out, Frank was a hoarder. It was not until many years later that I was able to delve into his extensive archive of diaries, correspondence, minutes, bills, bank statements, and other documents relating to the farming, publishing, and commercial enterprises he undertook. Perhaps he intended to use them as a resource for an autobiography later in life. Deprived of that opportunity by his sudden death at the age of fifty, I decided to do it for him. Through these papers and magazines, I was able to gain some insight into the determination that drove him to persist with his various ventures in spite of opposition, personality clashes, and financial setbacks. To some extent, they have also enabled the story to be told in his own words upon which I have freely drawn.

It is a story that took him from a North Country childhood and education, through the youthful pleasures and conscience awakenings of pre-war London, to the West Country, to an abortive venture in Ireland, a country mansion in Wiltshire, and to the urban environment of a radical town in Hertfordshire. It brought him into contact with some of his colourful fellow travellers in the worlds of organic farming, peace campaigning, and complementary medicine — including a few whose right wing beliefs seemed at odds with their radical ideas on ecology and health reform. It relates his determination to persist with his commercial ventures despite the numerous personal and fiscal challenges with which they presented him.

What drives one to stand amid a social torrent that's rushing in the opposite direction? What can those of us carrying forward the message of environmental conservation and food reform learn from the efforts of Frank Newman Turner and his contemporaries? Rather than rabble rousing, it is, perhaps, to be quietly reasonable and resolute.

In 1956, Victor Bonham Carter wrote of Frank in *The Sphere* magazine, "He does not, so far as I know, wear sandals; his hair is not long quite the reverse, he is rather bald; and he does not belong to the Great Unwashed. I know I have always been struck by his common sense and matter of fact manner and appearance." Though articulate and persuasive in his advocacy of natural living, Frank Newman Turner was not anarchic. He tirelessly carried a message that contravened social norms, but always endeavoured to remain respectable in his rebellion.

I hope that this memoir might serve as a sequel to his publications and reveal some of the characteristics that drove unwavering dedication to a paradigm that continues to raise its voice in the 21st century.

Chapter 1

Goosegreen Farm

It would be difficult to find a more diverse group of people as those who were tramping up and down the silage pit at Goosegreen Farm that day in May 1949. Some of the ladies were wearing what would be called 'sensible' shoes, with a skirt and twin set and carrying handbags; others wore riding breeches and a waterproof coat. The men ranged in sartorial taste from tweed suit and tie with gumboots (the popular term for Wellingtons in those days) while others wore the army beret, khaki jacket with buttoned cuffs, and boots, useful and tough working clothes from service in a war which was still fresh in everyone's minds. Alf Dyer, the farm foreman, was still there in his cap, shirtsleeves, and high waist trousers with belt and braces – most likely once part of his old Sunday suit.

They were compacting the silage (a task usually done by driving a tractor up and down the silage pit) at the behest of Frank Newman Turner who had applied organic principles to transform Goosegreen Farm from a costly and failing enterprise to a successful working farm. Now, having found that these principles were not only successful but also lucrative, he was passing on his knowledge and practical advice to a growing number of people keen to put these ideas into practice on their own farms and gardens.

In those austere post war years there was burgeoning interest in creating better health for animals and humans with food that was of superior quality (though this would be a contentious issue for years to come) rather than superior volume that farmers, encouraged by the Ministry of Agriculture, were seeking to achieve by pouring chemicals on the land. The alternatives to this – composting and the ecological approach advocated by Lady Eve Balfour and Sir Albert Howard in their books published in the1930s and '40s had inspired not only Frank, but also many others to seek an approach to farming that was more in tune with nature.

Frank & Lorna's wedding , June 1939. L-R Matthew Clark , Mary Turner, Tom Creyke, Frank & Lorna, Ella Clark, Geoffrey Turner, Joyce Turner

Goosegreen Farm, to which Frank had moved early in 1941 with his wife, Lorna, and infant son, was a 180 acre mixed arable and dairy farm on the edge of the Somerset Levels in the village of Sutton Mallet, at the foot of the Chilton Polden Hills. It was in a poor state when he arrived to manage it for a Quaker trust which had purchased it as a training centre for conscientious objectors who were required to work on the land. In the ensuing years, Frank had shown that 'organic farming', as it became known, could succeed and people visited Goosegreen from throughout the country, and from overseas, to find out how. Mostly they came for a day or two to see the practical applications of organic principles but the silage tramplers were attending one of a series of weekend courses at which they were given lectures and demonstrations on compost making, hay and silage storing, and the care of livestock.

Frank loading green crop for silage

Silage was a good example of maximising nourishment from the soil. It also had the advantage of being less vulnerable to the vicissitudes of the West Country weather. By harvesting the green crop, Frank believed, the nutrients were better preserved than in hay as a winter feed for the cattle. Hay was also produced on the farm but was allowed to stand out for longer than was customary by stacking it on a tripod system that allowed air to circulate beneath a mini stack (baling machines, although being invented at the turn of the century, were still financially beyond the reach of many small farmers).

Sixteen students, with their sturdy shoes, ex-army boots and gumboots, plus a couple of farm labourers were a useful compacting crew but their stint on the silage was just part of a busy weekend organised by the Institute of Organic Husbandry that had been founded by Frank as 'the world's first centre of instruction and advice on organic husbandry and organic treatment of animals'. It was part of an initiative to establish a foundation in memory of Sir Albert Howard, who died in 1947. As Frank's mentor, Sir Albert encouraged him in his experiments at Goosegreen and persuaded him to write about his experiences. It would be several years before he felt ready to present this information in his books (that were published by Faber & Faber in the early 1950s) but in 1946 he had founded *The Farmer* 'published and edited from the farm' as a quarterly journal of organic husbandry. By the late 1940s *The Farmer* had a worldwide readership and it was through this publication that people learned about Frank's work at Goosegreen and about the Institute's courses.

They had a full programme. After a Friday evening lecture about the principles of organic farming, Saturday was spent on the farm with demonstrations and practical instruction in establishing deep rooting herbal leys, compost making, preparation of the land for cropping, treatment of cattle diseases by natural means, and, of course, silage making. Saturday evening was given over to more lectures and discussions at the country house hotel where students were accommodated in the nearby village of Cossington. On the Sunday morning time was set aside for visits to local places of worship (an emphasis on Christian principals underpinning the Goosegreen venture had been set out by the trustees in the original manifesto for the farm scheme). Composting for the market garden was the theme for the afternoon with demonstrations of fruit growing and grafting followed by tea and homemade, wholemeal scones served by Lorna on the farmhouse lawn.

In the evening, a lively Brains Trust, with a panel of guest experts, and Frank's lecture on the economics of organic farming were offered. The course was concluded on the Monday morning by a final tour of the farm to clear up any queries that students may have had. The course fee for accommodation and all meals cost each person five guineas (£5-5s-0d in the old currency)

The Goosegreen visitors' book commenced with the names of students at that weekend course in May 1949. (It was, in fact, the second – the first had been held in March of that year.) It was signed by 16 students from up and down the country. Also present were Derek Randal, who had helped establish and run the Wholefood Society set up with Frank in 1946, and Rae Thompson, who would be a loyal secretary and general assistant to Frank and Lorna for many years to come.

Tea on the lawn at Goosegreen for Weekend Course students. Lorna (seated) and Rae Thompson, 3rd and 4th left, Derek Randal,4th right

Frank's work at Goosegreen attracted a wide range of visitors from all walks of life and all corners of the world. The organic movement was not just the province of gardeners and farmers – it had wider social and ecological implications that appealed to writers and artists as well as to people involved in health reform initiatives.

As we shall see, the management of Goosegreen Farm had been founded on Christian principles with a strong pacifist ethos driven by Frank's humanitarian beliefs. It was his own commitment to the peace movement, and his registration as a conscientious objector at the beginning of the war, that had brought him to Goosegreen in the first place.

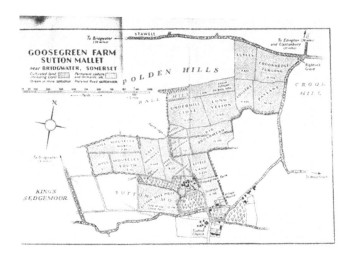

A map of Goosegreen Farm

Writers such as Elspeth Huxley, Reginald Reynolds and his wife, the novelist Ethel Mannin, the animal herbalist, Juliette de Bairacli Levy, and food-reformer Doris Grant, were all among the visitors to Goosegreen in 1949. They were followed in the early fifties by Fyfe Robertson, from the magazine *Picture Post*, Robert Waller, from the BBC West Region, and, in August 1951, Lady Louise Howard, the widow of Sir Albert who had been such an inspiration for Frank's conversion to the organic cause.

Sir Albert Howard himself had first visited Goosegreen in the mid-1940s and, following this, had immediately written to Frank:

15th July 1946

Dear Turner,

As soon as I got back from your farm I wrote to de la Mare suggesting Fabers should publish your book, and to Drummond saying that his bank might consider a mortgage on your farm in case you decide to purchase. I also told Drummond that he should get you to visit the Isle of Man and talk to the farmers.

At that time Frank was still renting the farm but Sir Albert had suggested he should own it to benefit from the fertility that he had built up. Sir Albert was keen that Frank should write more fully about the way in which he had restored the run down farm to successful productivity. Although he regularly documented his experiences in the pages of *The Farmer*, it was to be 1951 before *Fertility Farming* would be published to be followed by *Herdmanship* (1953), and *Fertility Pastures* (1955). As Frank wrote in his preface to *Fertility Farming*: *When (Sir Albert Howard) urged me to write a book about my work at Goosegreen, he knew that my full time occupation as a working farmer would make its completion a matter of years, yet he went to considerable lengths to persuade me that it was a duty that must be fulfilled. I shall always regret that I was unable to complete the book before his death in 1947, but he firmly deprecated claims and reports without the basis of solid practical results, so I have used this as a measure of all my work rather than rush into print with extravagant claims and statements.*

Readers of *The Farmer* and the students of the weekend courses would be among the first to benefit from the experience of the Goosegreen enterprise and they could not have anticipated a more practical initiation than trampling the silage pit.

In the 1940s and '50s the organic movement was putting down deep roots. The seeds had been sown by the traditional farmers and gardeners of many generations who had studied nature's interplay with the soil and the seasons. They learned how to use these natural resources which were all they had to work with before the rise of industrialised farming and the agrichemical industry. The emphasis of farming (and gardening, too) became a conquest of nature, particularly in those post-war years when it was believed that successful and adequate food production could be achieved only by intensive cultivation, forcing the land with synthetic versions of nature's molecules. They ignored the fact that the molecules that could be analysed and synthesised worked in a symbiotic relationship with a range of complex nutrients whose molecular structure was not fully understood nor identified, and it is these that are essential to the harmony of the whole process of growth and productivity. Furthermore, no chemist could create the billions of bacteria and other micro-organisms that play such a vital role in creating and sustaining the fertility of the soil. Those who nurtured the organicist seeds could see the folly of 'the rape of the earth', (the phrase used by G.V. Jacks to describe the deforestation of the Mediterranean areas during the Roman era)[1]. Many were expressing their concerns about the increasing chemicalisation of the land and advocating a more ecological approach, including such farmers and writers as Sir Albert Howard, Friend Sykes, Lady Eve Balfour, Rolf Gardiner, and Lawrence D. Hills, most of whom became founder members of The Soil Association, the organic farming organisation set up in 1946 by Lady Eve. They were also part of a wider health reform and humanitarian movement that had been active from the late 19th century vegetarian food reformers and continued with the community initiatives such as the Peckham Experiment of the 1930s. And it was part of the ethos that brought Frank Newman Turner to Goosegreen and would see him move, later in his life, from animal health to human health when he became a medical herbalist and naturopath.

The success of Goosegreen as a working organic farm had not come easily. Were it not for Frank's conscience and his determination to stand firm amid the clash of convention with non-conformity it might never have happened. That — and the Yorkshire grit in his blood.

---

[1] Quoted in Wrench, GT *Reconstruction by Way of the Soil*

Chapter 2

The Yorkshire Years

Inside the cloth bound cover of the autograph book are inscribed the words 'to dear Auntie Thirza. From Frankie and Joyce. Christmas 1915.' Frankie and Joyce would have been too young to write those words themselves so they were written in the neat hand of their mother, Mary. Frank was two and a quarter years old and Joyce one year old.

Frank Bocking Turner, Frank's father circa 1910

Auntie Thirza was the oldest sister of Frank & Joyce's father, Frank Bocking Turner. She was Frank's favourite aunt and remained so for the rest of her life. Although their use dated back several hundred years in Europe, autograph books were fashionable in Victorian and Edwardian England. It was customary for friends and family to write rhymes, verses, or sketches, the most popular of which was invariably 'By hook or by crook – I will be last in this book'. That was achieved by Mary Edith Turner, the youngest sister of Thirza and Frank Bocking Turner.

Thirza entered her address as Rockley Old Hall, Worsboro, near Barnsley. This was the family home, and she was the second of eleven children born to Newman Turner (himself born 19th March 1843) and Sarah Bocking (born 2nd March 1853). Their marriage, on the 14th April 1873, was 'solemnised at the parish church in the parish of Wicker, Sheffield, in the county of York'. The groom and both fathers described their professions as 'farmer' on the marriage certificate. Joyce, many years later, expressed the belief that Sarah Bocking was the daughter of the owners of Rockley Old Hall and Newman Turner their farm manager who later married her. He first got to know Sarah when working as a 'farm servant' for her father. After their marriage, they may have had a difficult period when, in October 1879, there is a record that Newman had spent a week in Wakefield Prison for 'larceny'. Fortunately, he was described as having 'no previous' and there is no subsequent criminal tendency recorded amongst the Turners (other than Frank and Lorna's fine for disturbing the peace on a CND demonstration in the 1960s, of which more in a later chapter). Whether the same can be said of earlier generations, we can only speculate, as our cousin, Jonathan Turner's researches have traced family lines back to royalty in several countries, including marauding Viking kings!

The Turners were of Yorkshire yeomanry going back at least to the early 19th century. It seems they were mostly tenant farmers. Perhaps, conscious of their age difference, Newman and Sarah wasted no time in raising a large family.

Thirza was the second (their first born, a son, died in infancy) and their fifth was Frank Bocking Turner, born on the 2nd August 1881. Little is known of his early years but, like many farmers' sons, he would have learned the craft of the landsman from an early age. A photo shows him in the ceremonial uniform of the 26th Yorkshire Dragoons in which he served from 1903 to 1913. He was a handsome looking man and caught the eye of Mary Ethel, the only daughter of Charles and Annie Clayton. She was 25 when they married on the 25th September 1912. Almost a year later, on the 11th September 1913 their first child, Frank, was born.

The Turners continued to farm at Rockley Old Hall, to judge by the address in Auntie Thirza's autograph album, but at some point, Frank senior and Mary with their children moved to Oldham House. Joyce's recollections, many years later, were of their childhood there and of Gawber Hall in the village of Gawber, two miles north west of Barnsley to which the family moved in 1925. *Oldham House was in a sort of row and there was a dining room – we always ate in the dining room for main meals because we always had maids. They used to be in the kitchen with the farm man and a student, if we had one.*

(Joyce Turner, interview 31st July 1999)

Frank Bocking Turner eventually had responsibility for three farms owned by a colliery company. Meanwhile they were blessed with two more sons, Geoffrey (born 1916) and Kenneth (born 1918). A fourth son, Phillip Henry was born in 1927. *My father was well paid according to those times – I think it was £5 a week.*

... he used to go trotting off in his pony and trap to the other farms and we were sometimes taken to school in the pony and trap on a weekday.

The family's move to Gawber presented new opportunities for energetic boys. The Hall was built in the 16th century but there had been a house on the site since the 13th century. The whole building consisted of a timber framework of oak beams held in position with wooden pegs and covered with ashlar stone. A priest hole was concealed behind the fireplace in one of the bedrooms and there was a pigeon loft to accommodate 200 pigeons. In earlier days, these would have provided a winter food reserve for the occupants of the Hall but now it was a tempting playground for the Turner boys, even though declared out of bounds by their parents.

There were, however, other distractions. The children had swimming lessons at Wombwell, a small town near Barnsley, and Joyce was taken to dancing classes in Sheffield by her mother every Saturday. There were farm horses, including one for the children, which unfortunately died, and their father, ever a true Yorkshireman, bought them cricket equipment. A meadow near the house became a makeshift cricket pitch. Grandmother Sarah Turner of Rockley Hall, used to send them ten shillings every birthday.

Frank went to Wath upon Dearne grammar school. Wath was a small town midway between Barnsley and Doncaster. While he was at school he and his brothers were brought up to do all the skilled work of the 150-acre ley farm which supported a herd of dairy shorthorns. Later, owing to his father's illness, he was made responsible for the herd on leaving school. For Frank Bocking, his wife's Roman Catholicism was also something of a thorn in the flesh. She succeeded in having Frank and Joyce baptised, but their father put his foot down firmly on the idea of baptism for his younger sons. (Although Christian principals remained strong with Frank for many years, particularly at informing his pacifism, he did not embrace the rituals of the Catholic church, choosing instead the simplicity of Quaker worship.)

The only thing that marred this happy childhood was their father's short temper. He used to take off his belt to the children (including Joyce) if there was any infraction of behaviour. As the eldest son, Frank had to bear the brunt of this and their relationship became difficult. Frank Bocking Turner liked his meat 'rare' and this may have helped to engender the Bright's Disease (a chronic disorder of the kidneys) with which he was diagnosed many years later. When his father was dying in 1939, Frank recorded the following in his diary:

Tuesday October 24ᵗʰ 1939.Received tonight a note from Mother saying that Dad is seriously ill with Bright's disease, but although the doctor thinks he may live for weeks he's not very optimistic. Each night since Saturday he has administered Morphia to enable Dad to get some sleep. This he has done in spite of a very weak heart, which does not seem very hopeful.

The doctor tells mother that the poison from the kidneys which results from this condition affects the mental attitude. For years he has been extremely irritable and bad tempered, subject to an almost continual state of depression, which had its repercussions on everyone in the family, particularly Mother. It now appears that there was a physical cause for this state of mind. 'I've often tried to analyse Dad's mental condition. I've never regarded him in anyway defective in that respect but somewhat deranged. This derangement now seems to have had its cause in something quite without Dad's control. While I lived at home I grew, like the rest of us, to disregard his tempers and complaints of pain, etc. as sheer awkwardness and even childish peevishness. We were usually glad when he went to bed out of the way. For a long time, he would never see a doctor even when his complaints forced Mother to insist on his seeing one. He said doctors had never done anything for him and he doubted they ever would. 'How tragically true that has proved to be now.

Whatever regrets the hindsight of later years may have provided, the atmosphere at home was one that Frank was glad to escape when he won a place at Leeds University Department of Agriculture in 1930. It would also be an opportunity to study the scientific basis of farming and dairying of which he had so many years practical experience.

****

Devonshire Hall, Headingley, Leeds
Sunday

Dear Auntie Thirza
I arrived here on Thursday, and intended to write sooner but do not seem to have had time so I'm taking the opportunity of writing now and also to thank you for the lovely calendar which you sent me. I have it hung up in my room now and it looks very effective as the room wallpaper is yellowish brown and thus the calendar matches it very nicely.

> *I was very sorry to hear that you have both been in bed most of the Christmas and New Year as I was expecting to see you sometime during the holidays.*
>
> *Joyce and I had a very happy day at Lane End during the New Year week and were pleased to receive your note.*
>
> *I'm afraid there is not much news to tell as it is only the beginning of term, I may be able to tell you that there is a shortage of money or something like that later on but for the present I think you will have to excuse this short letter.*
>
> *Hope you are knocking about again. If not, I sincerely hope you will soon be well to write to your loving nephew Frank.*

****

Frank took to university life and played cricket, rugby, and boxed as a middleweight or light heavyweight, for his years of farm work had given him a solid, muscular frame. A local newspaper report of a match versus Manchester University stated that 'F N Turner was the most powerful and finished boxer to appear in the ring. He beat P T Broadbent when the fight was stopped in the second round after his opponent was down for a count of eight'. As a middleweight, versus Liverpool University, his bout 'provided the most thrills …. F N Turner, who has much improved since his Christy contest of last year, won a hard hitting bout'. But versus Sheffield University he met his match 'F N Turner of Leeds, came up against a very fast and heavy man in H Cross, and both took a lot of punishment and at the end of the fight they were in bad condition'. Frank lost on points.

****

Bout v the future Duke of Hamilton

Many years later Frank claimed that he had fought a bout against the Marquis of Douglas and Clydesdale, who became the 14th Duke of Hamilton. The Marquis' mother was Nina, Duchess of Hamilton, who, as the Dowager Duchess, lived at Ferne, near Shaftesbury in Dorset, where she established an animal sanctuary and to which Frank and his family moved in 1953 to farm the estate.

It has not been possible to verify that such a bout took place, as, although the Marquis did win a boxing blue at Balliol College Oxford, and became amateur middleweight champion of Scotland, he was ten years older than Frank. Also, by 1930, he was a unionist MP, remaining in parliament until he inherited the title on the death of his father in 1940. Unless they held an exhibition bout, this may have been a fanciful notion on the part of Frank to add spice to his connection with the Ferne estate.

****

After obtaining his National Diploma in Agriculture at Leeds, Frank won a scholarship to attend the West of Scotland Agricultural College Dairy School at Auchincruive, Ayrshire from April to September 1933. There he attended lectures in dairy technology, chemistry, and bacteriology all of which were to serve him well in the journalistic work he undertook in the years to come. He graduated with a National Diploma in Dairying to add to his National Diploma in Agriculture from Leeds University.

****

Devonshire Hall, Headingley, Leeds – Sunday December 6th.

Dear Auntie Thirza

Was pleased to receive your letter last week. I heard you were at Rockley.

I did not get to the dance that you mentioned but I went to one on Thursday night and had a fine time. We are having one here at the Devonshire Hall on Thursday week and so I am looking forward to it. As you said in your letter it is very expensive here, money seems to disappear like smoke, it is a hard job keeping expenses down I'll tell you.

Our examinations start in a week so I have plenty of work to do now, I don't think I've told you what work we do. We have agricultural chemistry, physics and mechanics, agricultural economics and botany and they are all very interesting. Of course, we take different subjects later. We had all the professors from the University up to dinner on Thursday night. We had turkey and plum pudding, fish, soup, and biscuits and coffee. I'm playing football for the agricultural department on Wednesday, we are playing the leather and dyeing department in the departmental cup. I've not played any games for five or six weeks now as I tore several muscles in my leg and have to rest it until now. I expect I shan't be very fit in my next match.

We finish for the Xmas holidays on the 20th December and come back on January the 8th.

How are(sic)everyone at Rockley? Are things running smoothly yet? I think it will be better for Uncle Robby to stay at Rockley now don't you?

Did I tell you we had a wireless in the lounge? It is very nice to listen to the music at nights when our work is finished.

> *Well I think that is all the news for the present. I have lots of work to do so I will stop.*
>
> *Your loving nephew*
> *Frank*

****

Then it was back to the practical business of farming. He returned to Gawber Hall for a while before spending time on farms in Yorkshire, Norfolk, and south Wales where he was manager of a small dairy farm. In April 1934 he returned to manage the home farm before securing a job based in London. It was a final break with the north and his Yorkshire roots and the beginning of a life of cosmopolitan culture, the commercial side of agriculture, and a chance to develop his journalistic skills. There was employment which would take him to many corners of the country but, most fortuitously to Cornwall where he would meet his future wife, Lorna. And, with events in Europe taking a more threatening turn, he started to question the prevailing attitudes to militarism and explore the alternatives that were presenting themselves in and around London at meetings and lectures by thinkers of a less bellicose persuasion.

Newman Turner, Frank's grandfather, 1889

How did the Turners get the name Newman?

Franks grandfather was Newman Turner (1843-1908) and was probably named after his own grandmother's maiden name, Ann Newman. Frank, in turn, was given the second name, Newman, after his grandfather and became widely known by this name which has been adopted by subsequent generations of his family.

(Based on information provided by Jonathan Turner)

Chapter 3
London Life

For a young Yorkshireman, accustomed to the rigours of a rural life, London must have seemed an exciting prospect. Frank had, of course, had a taste of city life (and its drain on shallow pockets) during his time at Leeds University. London, however, offered cultural riches; concerts, theatres, cinemas, the parks and Hampstead Heath, and pretty girls. Not that Yorkshire was short of these but the proximity of parents, siblings, and maiden aunts must have been a restraining influence.

Besides, London was the place to be; it had escaped the worst ravages of the depression years of the 1920s. Up to 1933, unemployment stood at nearly 23% nationally but fell substantially over the next three years. Prospects in London were more promising.

With a university friend, Sid Forton, Frank rented a flat at 22 Belsize Square which was in walking distance of Hampstead Heath and handy for the West End theatres and concert halls. He soon took advantage of these cultural riches and joined Ealing Rugby Club.

In July 1935, he commenced work as an agricultural advisor to Farm Industries (which had been Hoskan,

Trevithic, Polkinhorn & Co Ltd). He was to be an introducer of feeding stuffs to farmers in Cornwall and Devon. He had to organise feeding trials with dairy and pig foods, supervise salesmen in twelve areas and undertake demonstrations and show work. The terms of his employment had required some determined negotiation on Frank's part. HTP offered him the job at a salary of £208 per annum plus car and expenses. He wrote back saying 'in view of the fact that the salary offered is no advancement on my present salary, I should be please to know if your company will consider raising the commencing salary to £260 per annum'.

Clearly, they admired his determination. The company secretary replied that the board would guarantee a bonus of £25 for the first year over and above the fixed salary, so he commenced work for them on April 1st. The first week was based in London with the Farmers' Marketing and Supply Company, visiting farms that were using their products and seeing the provisions that were made for their manufacture.

Frank's new Co-operative Wholesale Society pocket diary for 1936 recorded engagements in various parts of the West Country and further afield but it also revealed a busy social calendar. He could even note in the dying days of 1935 that on December 24th he caught the 2pm train from St Pancras which arrived at 10pm at Barnsley, 4 ½ hours late, where he was met by his brother Geoff. But he was back in London in good time for the New Year and there was a girlfriend, Joan Winter, on the scene. *'December 30th went to first winter prom with J. Eva Turner and Solomon. Beethoven's 5th and Bolero 'December 31st Sid's party at 22 Saturday 4th January 1936. All Blacks 0 v England 13 (Obalensky 2 tries). Prom with J, in queue at 6.15 – got seats easily. Peter Dawson, Eileen Joyce, Schubert's 8th, Walton's Suite for Façade, William Tell.*

****

> Dame Eva Turner (as she became) was an English soprano who gained world renown, most notably for her Turandot in Puccini's opera. Solomon was a distinguished pianist until, in the 1940s, a stroke put an end to his career.
>
> Prince Alexander Obalensky, who helped England to their first victory over the All Blacks, was a Russian émigré who became a British citizen. He later joined the RAF and was known as 'the flying prince' – for his prowess as a wing three quarter rather than his aeronautical skills. He was killed on a training flight during the Second World War.

****

It was a busy weekend, for on Sunday 5th January we read 'Joan to tea. First lesson in touch typing'. That would prove to be an important skill for it was in the 1930s that Frank laid the foundations for his journalistic and writing career. He became a regular contributor to a variety of leading agricultural magazines. From 1935 onwards, he wrote articles for *The Dairy Farmer* on such topics as 'Common Faults in Clean Milk Production,' a critique of galvanised pails which were unhygienic, recommending instead, pails with seamless tinned surfaces. Another article described the use of rubber in the dairy farm including rubber rimmed churns.

Given his later advocacy of healthy living the juxtaposition of his article on 'Equipment for the Accredited Producer' next to a quarter page advertisement for Capstan cigarettes at 10 pence for 60 cannot have been a happy one. (Frank was not a smoker although it was very fashionable in the 20s and 30s in cinemas, theatres, and bars, but a couple of early photographs show him posing nonchalantly with a pipe.)

Frank also wrote articles for trade journals such as *The Milk Producer and Retailer*, *The Milk Industry* (including ghost-writing an article by the President of The National Dairyman's Association in February 1938), and *The Ice Cream Industry*. For eighteen months, in his spare time he was the editor of *The Milk Industry*, a monthly trade magazine devoted to production and distribution of milk. The fodder for many of his articles was provided by his visits to farms throughout the South West and, by late 1936, he was writing for the *Farmer's Weekly* under the by line of 'A West Countryman' Amidst the trivia of daily life and work recorded in the diary were more momentous events of national importance, such as England's defeat of the All Blacks and:

Sunday 19ᵗʰ January 1936

Walk over Heath with Vic and Sid. Snow on ground, watched toboganning on Heath ---'Monday 20ᵗʰ January 1936

Snow gone, slight rain --- successfully baked a small currant cake --- King died at 11.55pm' 'Tuesday 21ˢᵗ January 1936

Prince of Wales now King Edward VIII. All BBC programmes suspended. Baldwin addressed nation, expressing sorrow at King's death

****

> The death of King George V was to trigger one of the greatest constitutional crises this county has known. Because of Edward VIII's wish to marry an American divorcee, Wallis Simpson, met with such widespread disapproval, he abdicated later that year rather than give her up.

****

To be in London at such times gave one a sense of involvement. *Thursday 23rd January 1936. Saw cortege with King George's coffin on the way from Kings Cross station to Westminster followed by King Edward, Dukes of York and Gloucester, Harewood and Kent. To lie in state until Tuesday morning. Eerie silence of huge crowd as cortege passed by. Evening at home alone. Tuesday 28th January 1936*

King George V's funeral. Went with J, Mrs M, & D to St James' Street but impossible to get anywhere near procession. Held Joan up and she saw it.

But normal life continued:

Saturday 1st February 1936

Rugger v Old Citizens won 6-3

Two weeks later after a long weekend home in Yorkshire to visit his newly married cousin, Gwen Elmhirst he scored 'the only try in the first half' for his rugby team's 18-0 defeat of Ilford Wanderers.

Apart from parties, prom concerts, rugby, and tennis, Frank took advantage of the wide choice of theatres and cinemas on offer. Radio was well established as a form of home entertainment and by 1933 over half the households in the UK had one, but TV was not introduced until 1936, so cinemas and theatres were extremely well patronised. Colour films were beginning to appear but the majority of the best films were still produced in black and white.

It was a short tube or tram ride from Belsize Square to the West End theatres and cinemas and, in the other direction, to the Golders Green Hippodrome where there was a regular programme of plays featuring rising stars and some, such as Flora Robson and Edward Chapman, already firmly established in the theatrical and cinematic firmaments, Sometimes Frank would go alone or with his flat mate Syd Forton. On one early visit to St Martin's Theatre to see The Two Mrs Carrolls, in 1935, he and Syd found themselves sitting behind Leslie Howard, who, obligingly, signed Frank's programme – a shrewd move on the part of a Hollywood film star as it probably helped to ensure Frank's attendance at the Tivoli Cinema in the following year to see him co-star with Bette Davis in The Petrified Forest.

For a time, in 1936, the companion noted on the front of Frank's theatre programmes was Joan Winter. At a time when forging a career was a priority and developing his journalistic skills, to say nothing of the distractions of rugby, tennis and cricket, romance clearly was not uppermost in Frank's mind. Joan Winter was a regular visitor to number 22 but on the 24th February 1936, he noted 'J round. Dispelled any idea of seriousness. Unpleasant but realised this had to be done as J was getting too serious.' They obviously remained on good terms as she accompanied him to more plays, although a Joan B also appeared on the scene accompanying Frank to several films and parties. But by 1937 a new and more enduring name began to appear in consequence of his regular visits to the West County. *Tuesday 14th April 1936*

3.30 train Paddington to Truro 10.10pm
Wednesday 15th & Thursday 16th April 1936 in HTP office
Friday 17th April – to Hayle
Monday 20th April 1936
With Clark. Tea with Clark and daughter

At which point, other than visits in the next week to a number of farmers in Cornwall and their orders for cattle feed, the diary is blank.

The farmhouse at Goosegreen,1941. (Watercolour by Hugh J. Schonfield)

Matthew Kinsman Clark was a tall man, good looking with a moustache and a military bearing which reflected his service in the First World War. He had volunteered in 1916 at the age of 32 and served in the 24th OCB Tank Corps, rising to the rank of 2nd Lieutenant on his discharge in 1919. In February 1912, he had married Ella Truscott Peters at the Parish Church in St Stithians, near Truro in Cornwall. Their daughter, Lorna Mary was born on April 27th 1916.

The Clarks had lived at Swanage in Dorset, where Matthew was the manager of a gentleman's outfitters and, in his spare time, acted as stage manager of Swanage Lyric Society's productions of Gilbert and Sullivan operettas while Ella sang minor roles and in the chorus. During the 1920s the family moved to Tregoney in Cornwall nearer Ella's sisters, Beattie and Ethel, and their brother, William. Matthew became a manager for HTP which was to become Farm Industries Ltd. based in Hayle, a few miles north of Penzance. Farm Industries, therefore, was the rather improbable cupid that brought Lorna and Frank together. The incentive to attend to his farming clients in Cornwall must have become stronger and Frank took lodgings in Truro in the summer of 1936

****

(letter to Aunt Thirza Aug 1936)
22 St George's Villas,
Truro
Aug 27th '36

My Dear Aunt Thirza
I was sorry to hear you had finally decided not to come. I wish I had spoken to my landlady before, then I should have known that she was unable to put you up here. I felt sure,

though that she would manage somehow so I had not bothered. I thought it would just be a matter of telling her you were coming when the time came. Even then I think it would have been rather expensive for a week's holiday. However, I expect I shall still be here next year, as my job seems to be developing very well, so perhaps we shall be able to fix something up in good time next year.

I think Joyce has arranged to go to Scarboro with a friend so she will have a much cheaper holiday and I think she will enjoy it better than she would have done here. I hope you will have an enjoyable time too – wherever you go. You seem to have plenty of people wanting to see you, and as I saw you when I came home perhaps it is as well you are giving someone else a turn. They may have thought it rather unfair to neglect them and come here, after you had seen me only a week or two ago.

The weather has been scorching down here during this week, and it has been very tiring. When it is hot down here it is almost impossible to breath. I shall be glad when we have a little cooler weather again. It has been so hot that the farmers are wanting rain again.

It is good of you to send the Chronicle. I enjoy reading about the places I knew. I wonder if you would be able to eat some Cornish cream if I send some.

All good wishes Frank

****

Lorna was just approaching her 20th birthday when they had first met for tea. She was petite and pretty with the permed hair fashionable with young ladies in the thirties in contrast to her mother's longer Edwardian locks. She had a pleasing soprano voice and, like her parents, performed in the local amateur operatic company's productions at Truro. Frank had to return to London, however Lorna was able to visit him there from time to time. They usually went to the theatre and he managed to choose plays with titles that furthered his romantic intentions.

At Easter 1937 they attended the Globe theatre where Athene Seyler and Edward Chapman were appearing in Thornton Wilder's one act play Love and How to Cure It (followed by Bernard Shaw's Candida). Frank had noted on the front of the programme that Lorna accepted his proposal of marriage on Easter Sunday. They celebrated their engagement in September 1937 with a visit to the Theatre Royal Drury Lane to see Ivor Novello starring with Marie Lohr in his musical play Crest of the Wave. On February 6th 1939, with their wedding set for the summer, the play was Quiet Wedding at Wyndham's Theatre. (He might have given more attention to the advertisement in his programmes for herbal products from Culpeper House had he realised that he would one day be a consulting medical herbalist at their premises in Bruton Street.)

By February 1938 Frank had moved from Belsize Square to Hampstead Garden Suburb. He had taken Lorna to Yorkshire at Christmas to meet his family as well as seeking the approval of Aunt Thirza. As he wrote to her later 'it was nice to spend a little time with you at Christmas although everything was rather rushed, I hope you liked Lorna. She was delighted with the way everybody treated her. She said she felt really at home wherever she went'.

Frank, however, needed to advance his career and later that year he secured a post as deputy supervisor at the Potato Marketing Board 'responsible for the supervision and maintenance of regulations governing the marketing of potatoes between farmers and merchants in the growing areas of the Home Counties and in London markets'. It was a step up but narrowed the scope of his agricultural expertise from cattle feed and dairying to the one staple of the British diet. But as he wrote to Auntie Thirza in November, *'It is very interesting work and I think, of all the Agricultural Marketing Boards, the Potato Board is the most popular because there is a minimum of interference with the farmers. The Board is growing and its powers are extending so the prospects are exceptionally good. In fact, on the whole I think I've dropped in for something really good – the kind of post I've been waiting for since I left Leeds'.*

With so much to look forward to, Frank's optimism was understandable but would be tempered by the challenges that lay ahead. Events in Europe were coming to the boil with the rise of Nazi politics and Adolph Hitler's expansionist policies and there was talk of impending war. In agriculture too, there was an increasing trend towards mechanisation and seeing farming as a war with nature necessitating chemical weapons, to force the soil to greater productivity and insecticides to confront pests competing for control of the crops.

In a world in which aggression seemed to be the favoured policy, both politically and agriculturally, there were two people in particular, who helped Frank to realise that there were alternatives that involved respect for peaceful co-operation with nature and with mankind. Canon Dick Sheppard founded the Peace Pledge Union and spoke at a number of meetings which Frank attended in the mid-1930s. Sir Albert Howard, a botanist who had been a civil servant in India, was a keen advocate of composting and farming without chemical fertilizers and pesticides. Frank had come across his writings, including his 1931 paper on the waste products of agriculture.

The ideas inculcated by both these people were to combine in taking Frank's life in radical new directions.

****

A bit of Yorkshire glory

England were playing the Australians in the final test match at the Oval in August 1938. On Monday, the news was spreading that Frank's fellow Yorkshireman, Len Hutton, who had gone out to open the batting for England on the previous Saturday, was amassing a big score. Frank managed to slip into the Oval on the Monday evening to watch Hutton reach 300 not out. The following day Hutton passed the previous record of 334 runs, held by the Australian captain, Don Bradman, who was the first to congratulate him. Hutton went on to reach 364 before he was dismissed. His record stood until 1957.

Chapter 4

Peace and War

Frank and Lorna were married on the 4th June 1939 at St Clement's Church in Truro in what was probably a relatively quiet wedding attended by family and friends. According to the local paper 'the bride wore ivory taffeta with overdresses of ivory lace and veil and carried a shower bouquet of red roses and trailing fern.' 'Bridesmaid, Miss Joyce Turner, wore ivory taffeta and a headdress of cornflowers and carried a shower bouquet of cornflowers.' Tom Creyke, a university friend of Frank's, was the best man and the reception was held at the Brookdale, a new art deco hotel on Tregollis Road in Truro.

They spent a short honeymoon in the East Lyn Valley on Exmoor, the setting for one of Lorna's favourite novels, Lorna Doone by the Victorian romantic novelist R D Blackmoor. She was as avid a reader – devouring novels by Walter Scott, Charles Dickens and Hugh Walpole – as Frank was a prolific writer. They returned to live in a bungalow at Well End, near Barnett, which they renamed Rockley after the family farm, Rockley Old Hall in Yorkshire. Frank revived his habit of keeping a diary, this time typed, and recording more fully his thoughts and activities, including those on the first challenge to the harmony of their relationship in the form of a new puppy .*Monday July 17th 1939*

Our young red cocker spaniel, Rogue by name, has been living up to his name with a vengeance today. The result was a fierce argument on the correct methods to employ in teaching the Rogue what he is and what he is not allowed to do in the house – whether on the carpet or in the corner! I say fierce argument, but it was fierce only in words and not in feeling. We both have extremely calm dispositions and after expressing ourselves strongly, for we have both strong opinions on many things, we go to great lengths to tell each other that we are not arguing antagonistically but merely putting a point of view. In this case the argument was as to whether or not the puppy should be smacked or just scolded when he had misbehaved. I said a slight tap should accompany the reprimand; Lorna said it was enough to speak firmly and demonstrate in a firm but not violent way that he must not do whatever he had done wrong. Well, we reached deadlock and the result is that we each employ our own method in dealing with the Rogue. His chief hobby in the house at the moment is decorating the carpets with small pools of water alternating with piles of something less pleasant even than the water. As Lorna is mainly responsible for going around after him with paper and disinfectant, I'm really quite happy for her to use her own methods of restraining the young rascal.'

If only 'a sharp tap on the nose' could have been enough to curtail Hitler and other European leaders. Frank always maintained that Stalin, Churchill, and Hitler should get into a boxing ring and sort out their differences man to man rather than sending thousands of young men out to kill each other.

He continued his active support of the Peace Pledge Union — even after the premature death of Canon Dick Sheppard, the founder — and had signed the Pledge in 1938. He served on the Executive Committee of the Golders Green branch of the PPU and became its chairman. In the late 1930s, there was much to occupy the peace movement with the mood of the government and, increasingly, the nation at large being one of belligerence to Hitler's expansionist policies. There were overriding arguments against aggressive tactics: the Christian and moral beliefs expounded by Dick Sheppard, and the widely held belief that Germany had been given a rough deal by the Treaty of Versailles after the 1914-18 war. This, many believed, had created an environment in which fascism could thrive. It did not, however, justify war, argued Frank and many others.

****

Treaty of Versailles

The Treaty of Versailles was signed on 28th June 1919 between Germany and the Allied Powers following the First World War. Under its terms Germany was required to disarm, make reparations for damage and loss inflicted in the war, and make significant territorial concessions, including the recognition of the independence of Czechoslovakia and Poland.

Some economists considered the terms were unduly harsh whist others were of the opinion that they were lenient.

(Source: Wikipedia)

Wednesday August 2nd 1939

After I joined the Peace Pledge Union, before his calamitous death, I was never fortunate enough to meet Dick Sheppard. To see and hear him on the platform, which I did, was to confirm all the saintly descriptions that those who knew Dick Sheppard gave to the man and the life he lived. Canon Sheppard, unlike most of his profession believed the terms Christian and pacifist to be synonymous, that it was impossible to be a true Christian and not a pacifist. Without any predetermined plan of organising a society or union he found one day in 1935, 40,000 like-minded men gathered round him as a result of a letter he had written to the press. He thought there would be some men in this country whose state of mind was sufficiently advanced to take the simple common sense attitude of renouncing war. He was overwhelmed, if indeed this calm courageous man could be overwhelmed by anything, to find there were thousands of men who not only hated war but were prepared to pledge themselves never again to support or sanction war. And so, there was no alternative but to bring these men into union, and the Peace Pledge Union was formed. At the time of its founder's death in November 1937 there were 126,000 members.

Frank expressed his views both in his active involvement with the PPU and in his writing, not just in his diary but in poems, short stories, and letters to the press.

The 'Enemy'
We know they're all plain ordinary men –
Forget their countries' name. 'What's in a name.', they're just
the same,
Our most respected playwright's pen
Convinced us.
When they toil to till the soil,
Their backs ache just the same;
They love their children more than fame;
From deeds of hatred they recoil,
As we do.
Their careless razors bring out blood;
Their heads are sometimes hairless;
They have their bad men – so have we
But murder will not make them good,
Or make them love us.
Frank Newman Turner

****

There were, however, lighter moments. In July Lorna's father, Mr Clark, manager of Farm Industries in Truro, was in London for meetings with BOCM, a major manufacturer of cattle feed, whom they represented in the West Country. Perhaps on the strength of Frank's connections with the Potato Marketing Board he somehow persuaded the directors of BOCM to include Frank and Lorna in an invitation to dinner at the Waldorf and a theatre trip they put on for their representatives. They dined well and as Frank wrote: *July 18th 1939*

Lorna took the seat of honour next to Mr Williams, BOCM Director, at a really delicious dinner which included: cold soup (savoury jelly), salmon trout, lamb and French beans, chicken and green salad, raspberries and cream ice. What the wines lacked in variety (white only) was made up in quantity and the waiters seemed to be doing a continuous circular tour of the glasses. We were extremely comfortable in stomach and mind to enjoy the delightful humour of Lupino Lane as a cockney turned Lord by the will of a father whose 'eye for a good filly' had taken him into Lambeth Walk one night in the dark Edwardian days. The show was 'Me and My Girl' at the Victoria Palace, one of the funniest we've seen for years.

One can't help wondering what mischief the Rogue got up to while they were out.

Matthew Clark had been a captain in the Tank Regiment during the First World War and we do not know how he felt about Frank's pacifism. He probably respected Frank's integrity and Christian beliefs and, above all, trusted him to keep Lorna's best interests at heart. Frank's own father and mother had, as he put it, 'dyed in the wool beliefs in the old methods of force'.

The time had come for them to make their first visit to their respective relatives since their marriage. They drove north on July 28th, a journey not without a minor mishap in the form of an empty petrol tank. *Friday July 28th*

Five miles out of Doncaster, within half an hour's run of Broad Lane, we ran out of petrol. The car just made the yard of the Plantation Hotel on the Great North Road where I felt sure I would get petrol. No luck, '...but there is a petrol station only half a mile down the road' the proprietor consoled me; and I set out to walk. After forty minutes hard walking I wondered whether the man at the Plantation was a fool or just sparing my feelings for a few moments. It was 10.30 when I tramped tiredly into a garage just outside Doncaster to find they had closed that very moment. But the boy took compassion on me after hearing my story. He offered to drive me back to the car in the garage runabout for which offer never in my life have I felt more thankful. This is a true Yorkshire spirit I thought and I decided to spend 2 shillings on a tip, — far more than I could afford, but I'd have given a pound if I could have spared it. Soon after 11pm we were greeted at the farm by the smell of a grand Yorkshire supper, the kind that is usually the reward for a hard day in the harvest field: roast chicken, currant cake, fruit flan, and cold milk or good strong tea.

On the 1st August, they went to have supper with Frank's favourite cousin Gwen, and her husband Alfred Elmhirst. Gwen's mother, Aunt Lilian, younger sister of Aunt Thirza was also in attendance. (Aunt Lilian was married to Henry Binder who was north of England ploughing champion in the days of the horse drawn plough.) Alfred had seen a letter Frank had written to the Manchester Guardian commenting on an appeal by the Labour MP for Ipswich for Britain to call a peace conference. Frank had written: *The appeal by R R Stoker, for Britain to call a peace conference comes as a much needed spur to a government which is forever declaring its willingness, nay eagerness to negotiate for peace rather than resort to force, but never does anything about it. ... Without condoning the methods employed by German fascism to correct the injustices of the world, I do feel that Great Britain and the Empire, holding most of the world's wealth and being the prime movers in the perpetuation of the present status quo, are therefore indirectly provoking German fascism.*

Britain, he argued, should be prepared to sacrifice to the cause of peace 'what she had made clear she was prepared to sacrifice in manpower and money to the cause of war.'

"Plausible arguments' said Alfred. 'I agree with you regarding the injustice to Germany and I am certain the national government of this country is responsible for the mess the world is in today but I don't think any generosity on our part would satisfy Hitler."

"I don't think that can be argued until generosity has been tried," Frank said. "I don't think our government is justified in arming to prevent an aggression until it has done all in its power to remove the causes of aggression; even then I don't think the policy of force would bring peace."

"But what about Munich? Didn't Chamberlain try the policy of conference and generosity then and wasn't he let down by Hitler's subsequent invasion of Czechoslovakia?"

"Generosity with someone else's property is no generosity and even if it had been Chamberlain's or British property that he had been generous with, the act was not followed through to its logical conclusion. In any case, whatever good might have been done at Munich was undone in the House of Commons immediately on his return when Chamberlain urged redoubling of our armaments programme."

Frank believed that Hitler's inference from this was that Britain intended to be strong enough to see that Germany remained where it had been put in 1919 so 'there need be no wonder at the events which followed.' At which point Gwen called Alfred out to some domestic matter.

Frank felt that Alfred might not have been at all sure that armaments would lead inevitably to peace but was less convinced that his parents' generation would ever reach a pacifist state of mind. They were, he believed 'too far sunk in the quagmire of the past'. Nevertheless, he and Lorna took his father and mother to the Harrogate Summer Conference of the PPU to hear Canon Stuart Morris, who was a successor to Dick Sheppard as the driving force of the PPU. Although Frank felt sure the Canon's personality would have been firmly impressed on their minds he was convinced that the abolition of war would depend on youth.

After the calls of family duty in Yorkshire, as well as another day at the PPU Conference, they set off to pay their respects to Lorna's relatives, experiencing the inevitable traffic jams that summer holiday journeys to the Cornish Riviera entail. *Saturday August 5th 1939*

As if to dog our day, and typical of local authorities when roads are at their busiest, a half of the road for a mile approaching Staines was in the throws of drain laying. Or perhaps the navvies had been instructed to dig holes in the road just to annoy the motorists hurrying down to Cornwall; judging by the expressions of some of the 5,000 motorists who passed through the narrow single line road through Staines each hour on that day, one would have thought that was precisely the intention of the borough council. I smoked two pipes of tobacco and wasted three quarters of an hour more time in covering a mile and a half through Staines. We arrived at Restormel at 8.30pm, again to be greeted in a manner

characteristic only of the county we were in. The steaming hot
Cornish pasties, almost nine inches long and five inches or
wider were followed on the table by clotted cream and fruit
with the inevitable pot of tea.'

Back in Barnet, Frank and Lorna must have missed the peace and tranquillity of the Cornish coves, valleys, and woods. Frank contemplated, during a lunch break from his inspection of the depots for distribution of potatoes in time of war – a task he viewed with 'intense distaste' – and the motto of Dick Sheppard came to mind: 'not peace at any price, but love at all costs.

The inevitability of war was on most peoples' minds, including Lorna's parents. Her mother wrote saying that Mr Clark thought that as things were looking so bad, Lorna should go back home to Truro. Frank wrote by return expressing surprise at the suggestion that they should leave each other so soon after their marriage. 'Assuming that war is coming' he said, 'there is not the smallest danger where we are, fifteen miles out of London in a completely isolated spot.' He added that he was convinced that war would not come: *Thursday August 31ˢᵗ*

Apparently, we are told the decision of war or peace rests with one man, Hitler. But the last thing Hitler desires is war, I said. For war would set him right back where he started; it would destroy all that he had achieved for the German people. He is too clever a man to let that happen. The only people who want war I think are that brutally minded minority which talks of crushing the German nation 'once and for all'. Such a sentiment besides being brutal and inhuman in the extreme is also ridiculous in that it is impossible. To talk of crushing a nation whose traditions are as deep rooted as the British and who's right to a seat in the sun at least equal to that of the British shows a surprising lack of understanding and a mind cruelly devoid of humanity.'

The letter must have arrived in Truro together with the morning papers which announced that Hitler had invaded Poland. *Friday September 1st*

Thick black headlines in the London evening papers gave the news that indicated that Hitler had at last taken the step which he had threatened for months, that is, to incorporate once more in the German Reich the city of Danzig, and the Polish corridor both of which were taken from Germany in the Peace Treaty of 1919...The news is grave, but I'm still optimistic. I am convinced that this step will deposit a settlement before any large scale operations are allowed to go on. Surely Poland, knowing how impossible it will be for her country to be defended, will not send to their deaths thousands of her nationals for the sake of a miserable frontier dispute which, to say the least, has been a sword in the side of European peace ever since the last war. My views of Hitler as a tactician have been considerably modified today. I was convinced that he was too clever a man to make war. However just his claims, and I'm sure they have much justice on their side, his methods of achieving them are as criminal as the methods employed by Great Britain, France and Poland for preventing the correction of the injustices. Once war starts the hopes of a just settlement for Germany are extremely slight. For that reason, I thought Hitler would not go so far. I was wrong.

The declaration of war against Germany was announced by Neville Chamberlain on September 3rd 1939. It stiffened Frank's resolve, reinforced no doubt by the fact that Lorna was expecting their first child. They decided to move to a bungalow on the outskirts of Barnet and entered into an agreement in March 1940 to rent White Cottage in the village of Well End, near their bungalow, Rockley. The rental agreement was for three years at a rental of £70 per annum. Lorna gave birth to me, their first son, in the new Radlett maternity hospital (reputed to be the first child born there) two days after her 24th birthday at the end of April 1940.

The cost of living for a newly married couple made inroads to an annual salary of £250.00 for a Potato Marketing Board deputy supervisor. My birth in particular incurred some expenses:

Radlett Nursing Home
Professional services 29th April to 3rd May £11-17-10
Mr C A Barnett
Professional attendance £2-2-0

Dr D E Green
Professional attendance £10-10-0
Birth notice in the West Briton 2/-

Then there were the day-to-day expenses:
The North Metropolitan Power Company, St Albans
Electricity to the 12th June 1940 £3-5-7 (including 10% increase)

John Line & Sons Ltd Wallpapers – 5 pieces 18/9
Barkers of Kensington
Repair of Philco Radiogram 7/6

The Post Office January 1941
Quarterly telephone rental £1-1-0
Bell rental 1/- (plus War surcharge)

It was perhaps, not surprising that something had to give. On the 13th January 1941, a final notice was served by Barnet RDC for payment of outstanding rates of £5-15-6. Frank paid it and was sent the receipt on the 4th February, duly signed on the 2d stamp, as was the custom in those days. There would be many more fiscal challenges in the years to come.

Having been actively involved in Canon Dick Sheppard's PPU for some years and becoming an attender at Quaker meetings for worship, Frank decided to register as a Conscientious Objector. He based his submission to the tribunal on his strong Christian beliefs:

Statement of Frank Newman Turner made May 14th 1940. "I refuse to take part in war not in contempt of King or Government, for I believe them to be as sincere in their cause as I, but in obedience to Christ who was the expression of God in all men and who commanded all who believe in God to love their enemies and to make them friends by example and through suffering rather than by force and coercion…I feel my loyalty is to God and humanity, above any particular portion of the world and I am certain that nothing can justify the taking of one single life in order to maintain or adjust artificial national boundaries, which God, in whose eyes all men are brothers of one kingdom, does not recognise 'I therefore claim complete and unconditional exemption from any task necessitated by military exigencies."

He attended a tribunal to justify his beliefs on the 4th October 1940 and on the 7th was informed under the conditions of the National Service (armed forces) Acts that his application to be entered on the register of Conscientious Objectors was considered and it was decided: "That you shall be conditionally registered in the register of Conscientious Objectors until the end of the present emergency, the condition being that you must until that event undertake the work specified below being work of a civil character and under civilian control …that you remain in your present occupation or otherwise engage in full time ARP work or full time work in connection to the land."

Within a few months it would be to the land and full time agriculture that he would return as his humanitarian beliefs and his agricultural training were combined to face the challenges presented by Goosegreen Farm.

Chapter 5

Battling Bureaucracy

Mixing idealism with the harsh realities of farming under the rigours of wartime austerity was never going to be easy. Add the burden of bureaucracy under which farmers in the early 1940s laboured and land and buildings that had been badly neglected, and one might have questioned the sanity of the group of Quakers and pacifists who purchased Goosegreen Farm early in 1941. No doubt the condition of the farm and its buildings determined its affordability at a time when financial resources were limited.

A.P.I. Cotterel at his home in Winscombe, Somerset

Goose Green Farm Ltd (the name was originally separated) was formed early in that year and registered under the Industrial and Providence Society's Act 'to establish a farming community in accordance with Christian principles'. A board of directors was appointed consisting of Harold F Bing, MA, FRHistS (Chairman), A P I Cotterell, MInstCE, Dr

Thomas Swarbrick, Crofton E Gane, FASA, W Parkin (Member of the National Council of the PPU), with Vincent C Burston, FCA as the Secretary. Frank was engaged to manage the project and he, Lorna, and I (in wicker basket, perhaps woven from similar willow trees to those that bordered the fields of the farm) together with Rogue, the dog, moved into the farmhouse in February 1941. At least we were well away from the danger zone of greater London which must have been some reassurance to Lorna's parents.

The trust published a prospectus for potential shareholders who financed the purchase cost of the farm and establishment of the community: 'It is intended that this community shall be an experiment in the rebuilding of rural England and shall be a training centre for those seeking a new life on the land and a focus of social and educational work of a related nature.'

It was set up to provide a conducive environment for COs who, like Frank, were required to work on the land but it had ideals that extended beyond these aims. Its objective was, for example:

'...to give training to those looking to the land as a vocation. It is not intended to provide a congenial asylum for those compelled to leave, for the duration of the war, other occupations to which they hope later to return.'

The farm's location, at the edge of the village of Sutton Mallett and at the foot of the Polden Hills, was close to Kings Sedgemoor on the Somerset Levels where a famous battle was fought in 1685.

****

****

The farmhouse, which dated from the 15th Century, might reasonably have been described as one of the ruins Cromwell knocked about a bit but for the fact that Oliver Cromwell himself had stayed there as the guest of one of his followers, Thomas Gapper, whose home it was at the time. Indeed, it was known as Gapper's Farm until at least the early 20th Century, appearing under that name in an ordinance survey map of Sutton Mallett, dated 1904. It got its newer name from the meadow in front of the farmhouse that was the site of an old goose fair dating back to the 18th Century.

The farm was 177 acres arable and grass, including eleven acres of orchards. It was divided into eighteen fields, each with its name, as was the custom with farms from ancient times. They were of varying acreage ranging from the smallest, Dowsey, to Underhill Close, and the furthest from the farmyard, Crookhedge Furlong. In the corner of Crookhedge Furlong, next to a crossroads, was Righton's Grave, where a highwayman of that name was reputedly hanged in the 18th century. Near the farmhouse was Nerber's Orchard and Pigs' Orchard. Across the Green were three farm cottages and a large wooden barn.

The Schedule of Dilapidations dated 12th April 1941, describes 'extensive deterioration of farmhouse and outbuildings. In the house, the attic ceilings had given way and the ground floor showed signs of damp in the passage and hall not sufficient to make renovation needful.' The state of the farm buildings, however, was more critical. The cowshed and engine house were badly dilapidated and the cottages in poor repair, the cider house, stable and closets were in need of renovation and the horse drinking pond was polluted by sewage and horse manure.

Faced with these challenges, Frank and the Management Committee had to get Goosegreen into viable working order with the limited resources they had at their disposal. As he later wrote in the opening chapter of *Fertility Farming*: *When I came to Goosegreen Farm the first calf born was dead. Disease was already master of the farm. Was I to be man enough to face such a master and turn his efforts to my own advantage? I thought I was, but disease drained the resources of the farm for nearly five years, ruining nearly two herds of cattle in the process, before I reached a position of stability in the health and production of the farm ...My training had been orthodox, and although my ideas had been modified by contact with, and experience of, the value of natural methods of farming and livestock management, policy was controlled by the owners of the farm, so the methods of the man who had farmed the place for the twenty five years previous to 1941 were more or less continued.*

Frank with Polden Dolly Daydream and newborn calf at
Goosegreen

With their limited experience of agricultural practices
(other than Dr Swarbrick who, it seemed, was himself a
farmer) it was perhaps understandable that the Management
Committee would be reluctant to break with conventional
farming policies but there were also the edicts of the War
Agricultural Executive Committee to be complied with.

****

War Agricultural Executive Committee

The WAECs were established in 1915 as a collaboration
between the Board of Agriculture and County Councils to
manage the country's wartime agricultural resources.

They were re-formed in 1939 at the outbreak of the Second
World War, with greater powers to serve orders on farmers

> 'requiring work to be done or, in the case of default, to take possession of the land'.
>
> (Wikipedia quoting Cabinet Memorandum. Food situation of the United Kingdom. 2nd October 1939)

****

Nevertheless, it was possible for Vincent Burston to deliver an optimistic first report to the shareholders when he sent their Certificate of Investment in the Society.10th October 1941.

Despite the unfavourable weather conditions in the early part of the year which made it difficult for the Manager and his staff taking over, we are glad to tell you that the hay and corn harvests have been very good, and that our apple crop is exceptionally good and proves highly remunerative. It is very gratifying for any member who can get to the farm at present to see our many ricks. The dairy herd of 33 cows is a source of steady revenue. The Directors are keeping the possibility of market gardening in view when war conditions relieve them of the necessity of producing all possible cattle fodder on the land. Repair work has been carried out, notably in connection with the cottages and the farmhouse and we can now appreciate what a fine old building the farmhouse is.

It was necessary for the house and cottages to be in a habitable condition. Apart from one skilled farm worker, Alf Dyer, who continued from the previous owner of the farm, Farmer White, there were seven men engaged on the land and general repairs about the farm buildings who were likely to have been trainees. They had to be accommodated, either in the farmhouse or in the cottages. There were also two women working in the house. The expertise of A P I Cotterell, as a retired civil engineer, was valuable is supervising essential drainage work for the farmhouse.

Goosegreen, view from the farmhouse towards Ball Hill, 1941
(Watercolour Hugh J. Schonfield)

The trials of the property and, what Frank had described in a progress report as the 'worst farming weather for 47 years, were complicated by the human elements of a group of pacifists strange to one another and, with the exception of Frank, strange to full-time farming. Some of them were unfitted either to land work or the more difficult task of living together. Alf Dyer, remained at the farm for a time but moved on to another farm in the area after a few months, so Goosegreen was run almost entirely by COs. Inevitably, there were changes of staff but Frank was able to report that 'we entered our second year with as harmonious a group of workers as we can ever hope, working all hours of the day with a keenness which equals that of the best traditional farm workers'.

The 33 strong herd of dairy shorthorns, sprinkled with a few Friesians, were producing about 90 gallons of milk a day and the farm committee were able to report that this represented 25 percent more milk from fewer cows and 30 acres less grass than the previous owner. Whilst the quality and quantity of the milk was considerable , the state of the buildings was not and the authorities insisted that they must be reconstructed and new sheds be built before they could obtain a licence for tuberculin tested milk. The farm committee also authorised the purchase of a pedigree dairy shorthorn bull to grade up the herd.

The reduction in the acreage of grassland was a necessary measure to increase the production of home grown food. The heavy red keuper marl of Goosegreen gave it the reputation of the most difficult working land in the district and Frank recommended investment in the purchase of a Fordson tractor with essential implements such as a double furrow plough, heavy disc harrows, and a cultivator. Farm tractors of those days were fitted with large rear wheels of steel with pedicles that helped them get a grip in heavy and muddy conditions.

This meant that some of the horses which had done the heavy work would become redundant. In his July 1942 report to the Management Committee, Frank informed them that he had had an offer of £40 for the filly and £20 for the old mare, Smart, which he considered a little below her value. They were both reprieved, however, for API Cotterell, in one of his regular letters to Frank said that 'Dr Swarbrick thinks it will be wise, in the present circumstances to keep, not to sell, the two horses. You will probably want all the power you can lay hold of before the 1st October.'

This last remark was probably prompted by the inspection and subsequent demands of the WAEC. Frank had received notice of their intention to visit the farm on the 24th July and advised API (as he was affectionately called), who made a point of being at the farm to accompany them on their tour of inspection. Major Parkes, the Executive Officer, Mr Wainwright, the Chairman of the Local Committee, and Mr England, the local advisor, must have been a formidable team of civil servants with the edicts of their Whitehall masters to enforce. At the farm EC meeting on the following day, API reported that: 'They examined the cowsheds but made no remarks; later they inspected the herd in the field and signified that the cattle looked well. In answer to their enquiry, they were given the milk output and figures showing how much it had been increased in total quantity and per cow on a much decrease area of pasturage. 'Walking across to Hill Mousley North they examined the root crops put in to take the place of the wheat ordered by the committee which had failed through wire worm. They made no comment on this. Then they went to the arable fields ......and their attitude changed. They were very critical of the state of the arable fields in particular Soggers and Rightons. In addition, they criticised our manager and referred to what they considered misjudgements, such as using the wrong tool on Soggers, although the manager pointed out that he had tried both and how he intended to deal with the thistles.'

After the tour of the farm, Major Parkes had taken API aside and said that he was very dissatisfied with the state of the land and '… had rarely seen a worse case.' He told API that, had they met the manager alone they would have taken drastic action, but as he (API) was well known they would allow a further two months in which to improve things. If there was no improvement 'they would advise the Minister to exercise his powers'. These included the power to confiscate the farm and place it under new management. It could, perhaps, explain why the previous owner had decided to sell it leaving it in the sorry state Goose Green Farm Ltd had taken on 18 months before. The committee were faced with two choices:

- To dispose of the farm and repay the shareholders before the possibility of the land being taken out of their hands;
- To carry on and do the utmost to bring the land into condition. It was better than when they took over but suffered through the labour difficulties of the previous Autumn.

The latter course of action was agreed upon and Frank was authorised to sell the two horses for £65 if he could get the price. That evening API drafted a letter to Major Parkes requesting him to state in writing what steps they required before the 1st October. He was conciliatory but pointed out the improvements that had been made since they took over the farm in March 1941. At the same time, he wrote to Frank, alerting him to the possible arrival of a letter from the WAEC and passing on Dr Swarbrick's advice to keep the horses.

There were urgent matters to be attended to and Frank and the trainees pitched in to meet the demands of the cultivation order received from the WAEC. His farmer's diary for 1942 records a flurry of intense activity – ploughing, hedging, and apple picking (the crop being sold to the Quantock Preserving Company for £300).'September 15th. Self-ploughed MC until 10pm in moonlight'.

Although there were by now 14 men on the farm, they were mostly trainees and a skilled farm worker was required. An advertisement was placed in The Bridgewater Mercury as a result of which Alf Dyer approached Frank. He was willing to return to the farm for a wage of £3.10/- per week plus a quart of milk per day and the use of The Nutshell. In view of Dyer's previous knowledge of the farm, the Committee agreed that Frank should engage him at once. Alf was to remain at Goosegreen for many years to come.

At the height of the harvesting season, bureaucracy came barging in again in the form of a visit by the manager of the Bridgewater Employment Exchange, a Mr Martin, and another official to arrange the transfer of three COs to other farms with the approval of the WAEC. Mr Martin was of the opinion that there was no need for a training scheme such as was being run at Goosegreen and that there were more men than necessary on the farm. The irony had obviously escaped him that at his visit, and that of the WAEC representatives, there were never less than two people in attendance.

Frank was asked to provide a list of men who could be best spared. The fact that two of these, Oliver Beckett and Kenneth Hollowell, were trainees did not please Mr Martin, but they were interviewed with a view to transferring them. Kenneth Hollowell, a quietly spoken and somewhat diffident man, was a solicitor by training and Frank had suggested to the committee earlier in the month that he was not well suited to full time work on the land. He was allowed to stay on at the farm provided he worked for his keep although it is not clear how long he remained there. (He remained on close terms with Frank and Lorna and later became their family solicitor, serving in this capacity for many years up to the time of Frank's death.)

Meanwhile, in view of the Labour Exchange officials' demands, API decided to go to London to seek advice and help from the Central Council of Conscientious Objectors. In a letter to Frank following his visit he reported that although the Ministry of Labour had the power to remove men, the Central Council of COs had found that they were reasonable at the top and they had already got in touch with the Ministry on behalf of the men at Goosegreen. API also wrote that he would be unable to get down from Winscombe, in the heart of the Mendip Hills in north Somerset where he lived, that month as he had no petrol. Petrol was one of many commodities that were rationed during and after the war and, on moving to Goosegreen, Frank had submitted an application for an extra allowance of petrol for essential journeys on farm business. (See application form) API, however, as a retired civilian, had to manage with his basic ration.

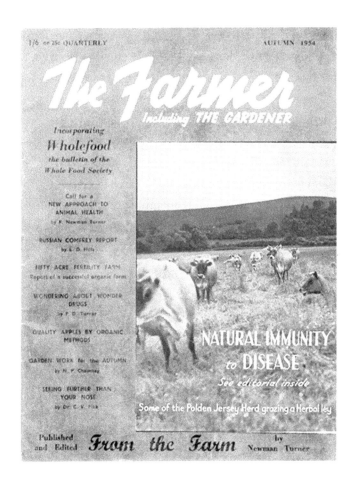

The Farmer cover Autumn 1954

By early October it was clear that they would not be able to meet the WAEC's deadline. The breakdown of the tractor crankshaft and the delay in obtaining a replacement had held things up. With the two pairs of horses working every day some momentum was maintained. Rightons, Soggers, and Little Land were all drilled. The dairy was yielding 60-65 gallons a day from 33 cows in milk but there was an outbreak of Foot and Mouth Disease in the district so the routine precautions had to be taken. All vehicles entering the farm had to be disinfected and baths for pedestrians to disinfect their shoes were placed at the main gates and both ends of the footpath that crosses the farm. This path was the route for the children of the village to get to and from the nearest school at Stawell on the other side of Ball Hill.

As autumn progressed the milk yield reduced to 48-50 gallons a day from 26 cows in milk but this was still an improvement on one year ago. Frank was also able to report that the crankshaft had arrived for the tractor after several weeks delay. By now they were considering a replacement for the old Fordson but a permit might have been required to do a trade-in.

Machinery was critical. The wheat sowing required by the WAEC had been completed but had failed to germinate, so Soggers and Little Land would have to be re-ploughed and sown again. This despite the application of manure and fertiliser to several of the fields. Rain proved to be a further hindrance.

With the harvest in, labour had to turn to the preparation for the winter rains with hedging and ditching. The ancient rhines could not handle the heavy rainfall and the lower lying fields to the west were flooded regularly in the winter. The WAEC offered grants for ditching, and prisoner of war labour was available for such tasks. An application was made and, in due course, a truck would arrive at the farm each day with half a dozen German and Italian men sitting in the back. They set to with enthusiasm and would sometimes arrive with wooden toys they had crafted for me.

The vicissitudes of the summer and autumn at Goosegreen with the weather, the WAEC, and other bureaucratic demands, to say nothing of personnel management – labour was short for essential work, some trainees having moved on, including Hollowell and Beckett who had been posted to other farms in Somerset – prompted Frank to consider moving on. Somewhat surprisingly though, and on his own admission 'without much enthusiasm for it', he applied for the post of District Officer to the Bedfordshire WAEC. He did not get it and would probably not have been well fitted to be a civil servant carrying out the edicts of the Government.

The local WAEC, for their part, had looked favourably on the improvements that had been made to the farm. When Mr England had made a further inspection at the end of November, they complimented Frank on the changes made. Nevertheless, the directors of Goose Green Farm Ltd evidently had their doubts prompted, perhaps, by the comment of Major Parkes following their first inspection that 'the manager was the real cause of the trouble. In his opinion, 'he was lazy and had no knowledge of practical arable farming'.

Without discussing the matter with Frank the committee placed an advertisement for a new manager for the Goosegreen Farm scheme.

Chapter 6

Rule of Return

Although he'd grown up on a working farm run on 'old fashioned' principles, Frank's agricultural education had inevitably been on very orthodox lines as had his subsequent employment in the distribution of cattle feed and co-ordination of potato marketing. It did, however, develop in him a critical faculty that later came to serve him well in challenging conventional practices. In the early years of the 20th Century agriculture was becoming more industrialised with larger scale farms supplanting the small mixed farms that could sustain a more balanced ecosystem.

After the First World War, the manufacture of nitrogenous fertilisers became more widespread, using a chemical process developed in Germany. Despite the Ministry of Agriculture assurances that productivity and profits would be increased by their use, uptake by farmers was slow in the 1930s. There was also a growing resistance to the Ministry of Agriculture's insistence that forcing productivity by the molecular mimicry of nature was more efficient than using the traditional methods. The change from small mixed farms with a selection of livestock meant that there was relatively less farmyard manure to place on the land. Thus, as now in many areas, farms became predominantly arable and with no livestock to be seen, the soil had to be force fed to improve productivity and support a monoculture.

The inescapable connection between soil and health was becoming an increasingly important issue in the 1930s and '40s. Sir Albert Howard had brought this to wider attention with the publication of his book *An Agricultural Testament* (1940). In this he had developed the theme he had first published about ten years earlier in a booklet he co-authored with a colleague, W D Wad, *The Waste Products of Agriculture*. By operating the Rule of Return at his farm in Indore, India, where he was Director of the Institute of Plant Industry, he had raised crops without artificial fertilizers or sprays. His cattle, which had grazed on these pastures, rubbed noses with those of neighboring herds infected with foot-and mouth disease, yet remained healthy. (This episode inspired Frank to challenge the slaughtering policy of the Ministry of Agriculture during a foot and mouth disease epidemic in the early 1950s of which more will be described later.)

****

Sir Albert Howard had observed at first hand the success of applying the Rule of Return – the application of compost to farmland – to sustain the health of the soil and the livestock fed from it. His method of composting, in which plant and animal waste was combined to achieve a more effective balance of nitrogenous and carboniferous material, became known as the Indore Process, so named after the institute in India at which he was the principal for many years. In the mid-1940s, Howard also took over the Newsletter on Compost which had been published by his friend, Dr Lionel

Picton, and he transformed it into the magazine *Soil and Health*, to which Frank contributed several articles. The last of these was in a memorial edition published in 1948.

At about the time that Sir Albert was conducting his experiments in Indore, Sir Robert McHarrison was making observations on the Hunza tribe of North Pakistan. Living in relative isolation, they had sustained a very balanced agricultural ecosystem for hundreds of years and were famous for their longevity and freedom from many of the diseases of western civilisation. McHarrison attributed this to their agricultural practices in which animal and vegetable waste was returned to the soil.

****

Whatever thoughts Frank may have had of putting into practice the recommendations of Howard, McHarrison, or Lady Eve Balfour, whose book *The Living Soil* had also been published in 1940, he was still obliged to satisfy the Farm Committee who, in turn, were conscious of the WAEC breathing down their necks. Their decision to advertise for a new manager might have been a panic reaction to the threat of losing the farm but it came as a shock to Frank. If he was to put into effect any move to self-sufficiency he needed greater control of how the farm was run. So, in the autumn of 1942, he had made an offer to rent it. This was sent to API and Vincent Burston, the secretary, with his budget for the coming year.

He followed this up in December with a lengthy letter to the Farm Committee expressing his grievances at their actions in seeking a new manager: *I wish to say how surprised I am at the manner in which the Directors are treating me, especially at this time when, in spite of the most difficult working conditions, I have just brought the farm successfully though an awkward situation and, I believe, saved it from being taken over by the WAC (sic). Favourable conversations with two representatives of the WAC, independently of one another, shows they are pleased with the way in which I have improved the farm, and although the improvements are obvious for anyone to see, I have not had a word of appreciation from the Directors, or even acknowledgement of an achievement which seemed almost impossible four months ago.*

He went on to refer to correspondence in which Burston had implied that they intended to look for a better man than Frank and, 'if this fails, they would fall back on him'. Burston also confirmed that the salary being offered was £200 to £250 according to experience, with free use of the farmhouse. '*Is that the highest form of appreciation which nearly two years of devotion and loyalty can produce from a group of fellow Christians, some of them fellow members of the Society of Friends? I am shocked and hurt more than I can say.*'

Frank then tendered his resignation with effect from the next Lady Day and, having done so, felt free to ask of the Directors on what inadequacy of his services to the farm they considered his departure desirable. And, middleweight boxer that he had been, he pulled no punches, citing the opinion of some trainees who had left that the Committee was following a policy of setting the staff and the management against one another. *Finally, if it is just that I should go, it is logical that the Committee with whom I have shared responsibility for the management should also go. It is reasonable to ask, would any but a pirate crew allow its pilot to steer them through*

81

stormy waters and then throw him overboard even to save the ship from sinking? Common decency and comradeship would rather that they sink together. The Christianity which we all share would certainly leave no other course.

This must have shaken the Committee. On the 16th December 1942 API wrote a glowing testimonial outlining Frank's achievements in reviving the farm. Although there is no documentary evidence, it seems that Frank and the Directors had reached some rapprochement. Christmas had given all parties time for reflection. Shortly before the January Management Meeting, Frank wrote to API to repeat his offer to rent the farm 'just in case the Directors are inclined at this time to consider it, for it seems to me, …as shareholders concerned for the future of the farm, the most certain way of maintaining the farm in pacifist hands for the resumption of the scheme after the war'. He offered to rent the farm from Goose Green Farm Ltd at a rental, sufficient to pay shareholders an interest of 3% and to purchase the live and dead stock at valuation. He sought security of tenure for five years. As Frank had an alternative offer to consider, the farm committee made a quick decision, for on the same day as their monthly meeting, Harold Bing wrote a personal letter to Frank and Lorna to say how glad he was that they had been able to reach an agreement in principle by which they would be able to remain at Goosegreen Farm. 'It will enable Newman to exercise more initiative in the management and development of the farm – a thing he has perhaps refrained unduly from doing because of the frequent supervision of the committee'. Arrangements were put in hand for a tenancy agreement to be drawn up and the live and dead stock to be valued.

Meanwhile the business of the farm proceeded and Frank had to use his initiative on one particular matter. The bull had escaped and had his way with three heifers belonging to the neighbouring farmer in the space of the hour in which he was free. Frank reported to the Committee 'I have satisfied Mr Baker's claim against us for damage by our bull by exchanging three empty heifers of equivalent size for the three of his which were served'. Nevertheless, he also reported that he had sold 'the old bull' to Mr Baker for £19. Presumably it was not the one who had gone out on the razzle!

Winter work continued; the willow trees lining the rhines had to be pollarded; the uninhabitable cottages had to be repaired; the order for a heavier Fordson tractor was cancelled in view of Frank's impending assumption of the tenancy but he agreed to purchase the binder that was on order as it would be essential for the summer harvest. The WAEC was approached to see whether they could hire a binder to the farm for the summer and they requested details of the acreage under cultivation and enquired whether Frank intended to use it to harvest for any neighbour and if so, whom. They were also asked for help with estimating the cost of drainage and ditching on the farm. Winter rains invariably resulted in flooding on the Somerset levels and the drive to Bridgewater became something of an adventure as roads and fields became indistinguishable. Regular dredging of the River Parrett and the rhines bordering the lower lying land to the west of the farm was essential.

On the 4th February, Vincent Burston had sent a copy of the draft lease setting out terms for the agreement between Goose Green Farm Ltd and Frank under which he could rent the farm for £420 per annum. It was an unpunctuated legalese agricultural document drawn up by a solicitor in Bridgwater but with certain restrictive clauses which clearly needed amendment. One of the main reasons for Frank to take on responsibility for the running of the farm was that it would enable him to experiment with the composting and other organic methods being advocated by Sir Albert Howard, Lady Eve Balfour, and others. Clause 9, specifying crop rotation and proportions, would have proved unduly restrictive and as it was could just as well have been a WAEC edict: 'To have the arable land at all times clean and free from weeds never sown with any prejudicial crop and never taking two white straw crops in succession and to farm such lands on the four course system that is to say, to have as nearly as the sizes of the fields will admit one fourth in turnips or mangolds one fourth in barley or oats sown with clover or other artificial grass seed one fourth in clover or grass sown in the previous year and the remaining fourth in wheat'.

Needless to say, the clause was removed. The inventory and valuation dated 25th March 1943 listed live and dead stock including 42 cross bred dairy cows and heifers, 23 head of young stock, 7 pigs, 6 ducks, and 3 hives of bees. There were five horses, namely Jolly, a brown mare in foal, Smart Jr, a bay mare, Smart, a brown mare, Peggy, a brown halfway mare, and Blossom, a three year old black filly. There was a list of almost 100 implements that read like a history of farming for the past 150 years and some of them had probably been on the farm for most of that time.

****

Goosegreen Farm

Inventory and Valuation

As at 25th March 1943

Implements (Selected)

2 farm wagons with lades

1939 Fordson tractor

Tractor plough

Horse rake (broken shaft and tines)

Massey Harris binder (frame welded)

Duck's foot drag (worn)

1Horse hay sweep

Winnower

Double screw cider press and apple mill

Harrison's turnip cutter

Rick sheet 10 x 12ft

Old copper cheese vat

Wooden cider vat

Seed fiddle

Harnesses, assorted

2 hurricane lamps

Bull staff

2 tons fencing poles

1 3/4 cwt barbed wire

5 milking stools

6 milk pails

Thatching needle

Galvanised shepherd's hut

****

In the stores were such feeding stuffs as calf nuts and dairy cake, 4 ½ cwt of binder twine and 75 gallons of sour cider, while in the fields and farmyard there was a 5 ¼ ton rick of meadow hay, 8 tons of mangolds, and 6 tons of silage. After deducting a sum for clearing weeds on the arable land, the whole live and dead stock was valued at £3,563-10-10d. A limited liability company, F Newman Turner Ltd. was constituted in June 1943 with Frank and API Cotterell as Directors. API had, from the outset of the Goosegreen venture, been a wise and benevolent mentor and it was considered expedient for there to be a connection with the farm committee as landowners and Frank's position as tenant. Goose Green Farm Ltd retained interest only as owners but were liable for repairs and alterations to the farm buildings.

The training scheme had been severely curtailed by the edicts of the WAEC and the depredations of the Ministry of Labour, whose insistence that fewer labourers were required on the farm, had presented a challenge to Frank in view of the added demands of increased arable cultivation. It was, however, his intention and that of the directors of Goose Green Farm Ltd, to resume training in some form for pacifists after the war. Under the terms of the lease Goose Green Farm Ltd also reserved the option to use about 12 acres for a market gardening venture after hostilities ceased.

Frank's other great ambition was to convert the farm to organic methods applying the Rule of Return. The health of the soil at Goosegreen left much to be desired and, although the health and yield of the herd had improved significantly and it had gained TT attestation, spontaneous abortion still took its toll and at least two cows had been lost in calving. Capital was raised by issuing debentures to pacifists and Quakers sympathetic to these aims and on the 29th June a sum of £3,688-13.4d was paid to Goose Green Farm Ltd in settlement for the stock, implements, and farmhouse furniture. API was a principle debenture holder in the new company along with another eminent member of the Society of Friends, Dr Joan Mary Fry, and, although API was now in his 80s, he continued to support the venture through the next few years financially and in person.

The labour problem was mitigated to some extent by the arrival of the German and Italian prisoners of war. They were delivered, literally by the lorry load, to work in small groups on less skilled tasks such as hedging and ditching, and fruit picking. They tended to be assigned to the same farm each day and as those who worked at Goosegreen became aware of a small boy playing in the yard with his spaniel Rogue, they would sometimes arrive with a model 'plane or boat that they had crafted from whatever wood they could find in the abundant spare time they had in their camps. The two nearest of these were at Colley Lane in Bridgwater and near the village of Goathurst, just to the south. Goathurst Camp housed mainly Italian prisoners captured in the Desert Campaign and one of these was Antonio Capozzoli who had served in Abyssinia. 'Tony' showed an aptitude as a cowman and eventually was allowed to stay at the farm as there was room to spare in the farmhouse.

****

Italian and German Prisoners of War

There were a number of POW camps situated in Somerset and the one outside the village of Goathurst, a few miles to the south of Bridgwater, housed about 300 Italians who had been captured in the Desert Campaign of North Africa. They slept in Nissen huts, constructed of corrugated metal sheets bent to a half cylinder with each end in the ground.

Those who were willing to, worked on the land and, called 'co-operators,' were taken in the backs of lorries, twenty at a time to work on farms in the surrounding area where they were put to hedging and ditching and other less skilled tasks. They were given a ration of one packet of cigarettes a week and earned tokens worth a few pence a week. Prisoners were allowed to write home but letters had to remain unsealed for censoring, as they were not to reveal where they were located.

Some were permitted to stay on the farms where there was accommodation available and could earn their keep. Their distinctive brown uniforms with yellow flashes made them easily recognisable to the police if they wandered beyond a five mile radius of the farm on which they worked.

****

On one occasion, when Lorna and I were staying with her parents in Cornwall, Frank wrote to her relating an incident that illustrated the military mindset of the prisoners that was at variance with Frank's pacifist ethos: *'Rogue has taken to going up into Tony's room and sleeping on his bed whenever he can find the door open – much to Tony's amusement. Tony was in the process of making a gun for Roger when I came home from Bristol the other night. When I tactfully said I didn't like guns – that there were too many of them in the world already he said it was only for a joke – not a real one. I said that many things started like that and that I would rather see all such things abolished. He said they would be after this war. If England wins he said they are going to finish such things and if Germany wins they are going to do the same, so that whichever side wins there is going to be no more war. Well I hope he's right and I said so. I suppose he ought to know something about it as he's been on both sides and it looks as though both sides are aiming at the same thing. I wonder when they'll discover that? Perhaps when there's nothing left of anything. I asked him instead to make Roger a little trolley that he could be ridden about in – the sort of thing you wanted. He will make it as soon as we can get some suitable wood for the wheels'.*

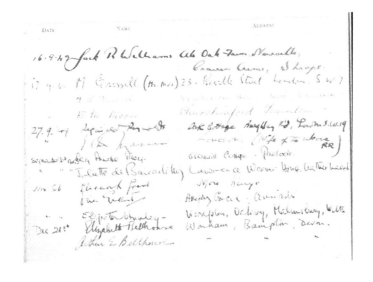

A page from the Goosegreen visitors' book, 1949

A page from the Goosegreen visitors' book, 1951

After the war Tony stayed on at Goosegreen as a cowman and general farmhand. He was later joined by his wife and three children who emigrated from their home in Naples to live in one of the farm cottages across the green from the farmhouse. Every so often, a torrent of Italian expletives and the sound of flying pots and pans would float across the green as the Latin temperament of their small community boiled over.

Medical Testament

In March 1939, a group of doctors based in Cheshire published a critique of health policy in the British Medical Journal, arguing that, while advances in confronting disease were receiving much attention, the question of prevention could only be addressed by looking to the health of the soil. The driving force of the Medical Testament was Dr. Lionel Picton who had published the Newsletter on Compost, later transformed into the magazine *Soil and Health* by Sir Albert Howard. Other supporters of this Cheshire Panel Committee's initiative were Sir Robert McHarrison, Lady Eve Balfour, and Scott Williamson and his wife Innes Pearce, two doctors who had established the Pioneer Health Centre in Peckham, south London.

End 8:00 Am   April 8, 2023

Chapter 7

Ethos, Ethics, and Environment

There might be a certain irony in the presence of soldiers (albeit captive) working on a farm run by pacifists for pacifists, but Frank and Lorna always applied the highest Christian principles to their dealings with them, providing them with food and other provisions whenever they came to the farm.

According to Philip Conford, in *The Development of the Organic Network* (2011, page 100), the pioneers of the organic movement attached great importance to understanding the Laws of Nature, and, in many cases this was underpinned by a strong religious faith. This was certainly true of Frank whose pacifism was driven by the same ethos. As he later wrote in *Fertility Farming*: *We are but the tenants of life, having on loan the physical from the earth and the spiritual from God. What happens to our spiritual being and its inspiration remains to be discovered after we lay down the physical life. But our duties regarding the physical body and its means of natural sustenance are clear to all. It must be returned, together with all organic matter derived from the earth, back to the earth.*

(Fertility Farming, 1951. P 39)

Setting aside the practical benefits of working with nature for the betterment of soil fertility it may be instructive to examine the influences that ignited his pacifism. In as much as an agricultural background can be regarded as normal, Frank had a fairly conventional childhood. His mother, Mary, was a catholic and imbued in her children strong Christian principles. But most of the major religions sanctioned war as a necessary evil, accepting the edicts of the state and blessing its perpetrators. We have already seen how he realised that the ideals of the Peace Pledge Union fell on deaf ears with his parents' generation. I assume it must have been some search for deeper meaning to his early religious upbringing that prompted him to attend the sermons of Canon Dick Sheppard at St. Pauls and the early meetings of the PPU in the turbulent political times of the mid-1930s. He had also read *A Testament of Youth*, Vera Brittain's autobiographical account of life during the First World War. Her experience of personal loss (her brother, close friends, and her fiancé all killed in the conflict) and as a nurse on the Western Front had been a powerful influence in forming her own pacifist beliefs. Frank had written to her inquiring as to the progress of her next book (*A Testament of Friendship*, 1940) and amongst his papers is a gracious reply from her typed with a green typewriter ribbon.

In 1940, Frank also acquired a set of small volumes, translations of the works of Leo Tolstoy. In one of these '*What Then Must We Do?*' (first published in 1886) he had underlined a passage of particular significance: *Science has a very definite aim, which it attains. That aim is to maintain superstition and deception among the people and thereby hinder the progress of humanity towards truth and welfare.*

There has long existed, and still exists, a terrible superstition which has done almost more harm than the most fearful religious superstitions… This superstition is quite similar to the religious superstitions: it consists in the assertion that, besides man's duty to man, there exist yet more important obligations to an imaginary being. For theology, this imaginary being is God, but for political science it is the State. The religious superstition consists in this, that sacrifices, sometimes of human lives, to this imaginary being are necessary, and men may and should be brought to them by all means, not excluding violence. The political superstition consists in this, that besides the duties of man to man there exist more important duties to the imaginary being, and that sacrifices, very often of human life, offered up to this imaginary being, the State, are also necessary, and that men may and should be brought to them by all possible means not even excluding violence. This superstition, formerly supported by the priests of various religions, is now supported by so called science.

(What Then Must We Do? by Leo Tolstoy, trs. Aylmer Maude, 1935, OUP)

What the extent of Frank's belief in 'the imaginary being' had been it is difficult to say; in his writing, he had often used the imagery of God in his references to the spiritual dimension though it could equally have been a surrogate for Nature. The family's arrival in Somerset presented an opportunity to become members of the Society of Friends (Quakers) whose contemplative form of worship provided an alternative to the more formalised rituals of the mainstream religions. Meeting for Worship provided an escape into one's own thoughts, which, in Franks case, must often have been on the more practical matters of the farm than the spiritual.

The report to the shareholders of Goosegreen Farm Ltd in 1944, was able to announce that the electric milking machine with all its accessories had been installed and the herd had gained its TT attestation. A contract had been placed with the Somerset Rivers Catchment Board for dredging of the ditches and a grant had been received from the Ministry of Agriculture for half the cost of £750. The following year Frank, was able to report that this had been completed and was beneficial in view of the exceptional rainfall during the winter.

Bringing balance back to the land and livestock did not, however, immediately guarantee a healthy bank balance. Contagious abortion, with which Frank had been struggling since he commenced management of the farm, had depleted the stock and resulted in a decline of milk output as well as increased veterinary fees. At his request, the Directors agreed to a remission of some rent and, to increase milk production, API proposed that he should purchase, on his own account, five Milkers and let them to Frank on hire purchase payable by twelve monthly instalments of £30. All this reinforced Frank's conviction that he needed to apply a radically different approach if he was to curtail costs and improve health and fertility on the farm. *The fact that not all the cattle succumbed to contagious abortion led me to believe that it was not primarily a disease caused by bacteria, but a deficiency disease and the bacteria a secondary factor. The farm had been an orthodox dairy farm and the cattle had lived and produced milk on the same pastures for generations. They had been forced in the usual manner with concentrated manufactured foods. The more milk the cows gave, the less natural bulky food they were allowed to eat – what home grown food they had was raised with artificial fertilizers. For my predecessor was a good farmer and the hall mark of a good farmer was a large artificial fertilizer bill.*

(*Soil and Health*, Summer 1946)

Reviving the depleted soil of Goosegreen and the precarious health of the livestock had also taught him another powerful lesson: *The only way we can repair the harm we have done is to give nature a chance to work in her own way and, as far as we must interfere by way of farming and gardening, let it be in imitation of nature rather than battle against nature.*

Working with nature in a collaboration of mutual respect, rather than a constant effort at subjugation, also meant for Frank applying an ethos of compassion for all life. Soon after their arrival at Goosegreen in 1941, he and Lorna decided to become vegetarians. This was primarily a humanitarian decision although there were other influences as he later explained in an article he wrote entitled Why I am a Vegetarian Farmer.

"It was Christmas 1941 that brought an end for me to the task of tearing apart the tissues of my fellow creatures. My teeth were, in any case, rarely equal to the task after struggling with knives that were only occasionally sharp enough to reduce these animal organs sufficiently small to pass though my alimentary tract...On this Christmas, I was a happy and well fed farmer keeping a wide variety of happy and over fed animals – among which were numerous ducks, geese, cockerels, and pigs. Christmas, the traditional time of

nemesis for these unsuspecting creatures, brought me the task of slaughtering twenty or thirty ducks and geese which I had sold to a nearby poulterer. The price had been good – it was during the war when high prices were paid for poultry by merchants who travelled from farm to farm outbidding one another for the victims of the mass slaughter by which Christian people celebrate the birth of their Prince of Peace. As I took these helpless, pathetic creatures in my firm grip and one by one violently squeezed the life from their beautiful bodies, I suddenly released my mind and opened my eyes. And I saw in the eye of the creature, which now pleaded with an expression I could hardly bear, the power of the life was in me and which I realised was also in that suffering bird, but which was within the power of neither of us to create. That moment when I saw the soul of a fellow creature my mind was freed from the bondage of a tradition which monopolised the God given attributes of man. No argument of man could, from that moment, stand for me against the question in those haunting eyes. For it was a question to which there could be but one answer, whether you have looked into the eyes of a creature drawing its last precious breath, or whether you are sitting face to face with the juicy steak you consider essential to your nutritional welfare. Have you or I the right to destroy any life which was never ours to give whatever we may be driven to do in self-defence? Life to give or take is not in the power or knowledge of man. This I knew more surely than anything I had ever known, and that Christmas time was an appropriate time to give it effect. I had eaten my last meal from the flesh of my fellow creatures."

"But I was a farmer! What did this decision mean? Pigs were on the farm for no other reason than their fattening for *slaughter. So, they had to go, to someone who had not seen into those eyes with an alert and open mind. But my decision regarding pigs was made easier by an incident which allowed my deepest farming instincts, which had hitherto held control of my emotions, to rationalise on the level of hard economy."*

"Early that spring we had two acres of beautiful lettuce which had been nursed through the winter until each lettuce had reached a crisp and saleable condition, just when the lettuce was scarce and prices consequently at their highest. It was the first time I had succeeded in maturing a luxury crop at the 'right' time from the point of view of money making. The whole crop was worth £200 – a useful sum for such a small patch of land to a farmer accustomed to cereal crops at £20 an acre at that time. At last something had succeeded and I had learned one way to reasonably make money. I went away from the farm with my family for a day or two and enjoyed the prospects of success. But I returned to the spectacle of destruction such as only the ruthless snout of a pig could achieve. The whole two acres of lettuces had been reduced to broken shells of outer leaves. The doors of the piggeries had been left open and all the pigs had got out and, working the lettuce crop row by row, moved systematically up and down the field and eaten the heart of practically every lettuce. That was the end of my success as a market gardener – at any rate for that year."

"The pigs were sold and we kept no more. My most satisfying farming enterprise had gone. And my pocket would be much the lighter. But my conscience too was lighter and the burden of breeding and feeding for the sole purpose of slaughter was lifted from my mind."

(Why I am a Vegetarian Farmer (Undated))

Just as it was imperative to tackle disease on the farm by building up better health in the soil and thereby better nutrition for the cattle, so he and Lorna applied the principles of nature cure to their family for their medical care. They consulted an American trained naturopath in Bristol regarding Lorna's exhaustion as well as some digestive problems Frank had been experiencing. Mr Regan even made some homoeopathic recommendations for a Jersey bull which had tested positive for TB. The bull was placed in isolation from the rest of the herd, fasted, and treated with enemas and homoeopathic remedies and made a full recovery, testing negative before returning to his duties in the herd.

****

Nature cure was gaining in popularity in England, thanks to the success of the 1936 book *Everybody's Guide to Nature Cure* by the naturopath Harry Benjamin and the fame of Stanley Lief at whose Champneys Nature Cure Clinic, near Tring in Hertfordshire, many chronically sick patients had been restored to health. A similar clinic had been established by Swiss nature doctor, Dr Max Bircher Benner in Zurich. Bircher Benner was best known as the creator of meusli, a breakfast food composed of soaked oatmeal, grated apple, raisins, nuts and seeds, and copied and much distorted by commercial cereal manufacturers many years later.

****

When Lorna was expecting their second child in 1945, they learned about Stonefield Maternity Home in Blackheath, where natural childbirth was offered for the growing number of parents who decided the gentler, less intrusive approach that they offered was preferable. Stonefield also had a lower incidence of puerperal fever and toxaemia than many other maternity homes. The home was run by the somewhat pastel named partnership of Dr Pink and Dr White.

Dr Cyril Pink, painted by Elva Blacker (from her exhibition catalogue)

Dr Cyril Pink was a Theosophist and a disciple of Dr Max Bircher Benner, and had written *The Ideal Management of Pregnancy* 1930, (later reissued as *Foundations of Motherhood*) and *Diet in Relation to Pregnancy* (1932). It is quite likely that Frank and Lorna had read these. As luck would have it, Stonefield maternity home was evacuated during the war to Wookey Hole at the foot of the Mendip Hills in Somerset, and it was there, on the 12th June 1945, that their second son, Giles, was born.

Cyril Pink and his wife, Marguerite, a midwife, became firm friends of Frank and Lorna and visited Goosegreen, and later Ferne on a number of occasions. He also wrote a regular column for *The Farmer*.

****

> ### Dr Cyril Pink (1894-1965)
>
> The term 'natural childbirth' was coined by the obstetrician, Dr Grantley Dick Read, but it was Dr Cyril Pink, who, in his 1932 publication *Diet in Relation to Pregnancy*, had set out its principles. He advocated a minimum of medical intervention, a vegetarian diet of fruit, vegetables, salads, and nuts as the best possible protection against abnormalities in pregnancy and birth. But with his Theosophist leanings , he believed vegetarianism went beyond its health benefits and embodied the caring qualities of femininity. A simple, natural diet, as advocated by Dr Max Bircher Benner, and other food reformers from the late 19th century onwards, would encourage qualities that made for good citizenship and world peace. His book, *Foundations of Motherhood* (1947) became an influential guide for the post war 'baby boomer' generation.

****

The ethos of eschewing the consumption of animal flesh, both as a humanitarian decision and a practice more in tune with the ideals of peaceful co-existence was something Frank and Lorna shared with the Pinks. They were realistic enough, however, not to proselytise about it and the irony cannot have escaped them that Adolph Hitler was a vegetarian (though by more recent revelations, not a particularly healthy one) who sanctioned the most appalling barbarities against his fellow creatures. But, just as pacifist leanings were by no means universal among environmentalists and proponents of organic husbandry, so food reform was not widespread among those who campaigned for peace and a better world order. Frank was of the opinion that the ethics of individual conduct guided by what he called 'the ideal of Jesus', had been subordinated to the actions of the State. 'When individual man has been organised into groups or states, and the individual has been merged into the mass, the guiding principles for the individual have failed to function for the mass.

Where it is regarded as wrong for the individual to murder, on his own initiative – merely to take life without inflicting the slightest suffering – if this is done at the behest of the organised mass of individuals, the nation state, and with extreme violence and infliction of the most horrible agonies, the act is commended as a grand and glorious thing.'

Even before the war he wanted to see a group of people willing to retain their individuality but to work together without the 'morass of state regimentation.' 'Such a community of individuals will extend the example of Jesus into the behaviour of an organised group and so demonstrate that pattern of nationhood, the absence of which has brought the existing nations of the world into the present state of organised un-holiness.'

Frank's inspiration for this was his acquaintance with Hugh J Schonfield, who with his wife Helene, hosted meetings of the Golders Green Peace Pledge Union of which Frank was Chairman. Schonfield, a Hebrew Christian, was an eminent bible scholar and the author of a number of books on the development of the Christian religion. In his book *The Politics of God* (1970) he describes how, in 1938, strolling in his then garden in Staines, he experienced a revelation: *Suddenly I was in the midst of a stream of light which poured upon me from every direction, all the colours of the rainbow, so that my surroundings completely disappeared. Inwardly I heard words which came from the book of the Hebrew prophet Zachariah, Not by might, nor by power, but by my spirit. At the same time, it was conveyed to my mind that what was called for the deliverance of humanity was a servant nation. It was the building of this nation to which I was required to address myself.*

(The Politics of God (1970) Prologue p xiv. Ed. Stephen A Engelking (2012) The Hugh & Helene Schonfield World Service Trust, Tuningen, Germany.)

Schonfield set about fulfilling his mission by founding the Society for the Constitution of a Holy Nation in September 1940 and invited Frank to be his Vice President. Its objectives were: *to create by the will of God, as an instrument for the promotion of world peace and justice, a free nation, pervasive and universal, dedicated to the service of humanity, to the function of international mediation, and to the demonstration of a pattern of nationhood.*

(Also appearing on the letterhead as 'Field Secretary', was a young actor named Derek Randal who would, after the war, find his way to Goosegreen to assist Frank with his wholefood initiatives.)

In a conference, held in September 1941, it was decided to rename the society The Service Nation Movement to tone down the religious flavour of the original title.

Although the move to Goosegreen cut them off from the activities of the movement, Frank remained nominally on the committee for several years. Hugh and Helene Schonfield, with their children, also visited Goosegreen for short vacations during which Hugh would relax by painting watercolours of the farm. Frank had also arranged for Hugh to address the Bridgwater branch of the Society of Friends at the Quaker Meeting House. With Frank in the chair, Hugh Schonfield described how the League of Nations had failed to avert the present crisis (the war) because of the divided nationalistic loyalties of its representatives. He then explained how he hoped that the service nation movement might bring together a group of 'world citizens' having no national ties, able to act in the service of mankind and in the mediation of international disputes.

Unfortunately, it was not by mediation or by spirit but by power that the war was brought to an end in 1945. In the view of many pacifists, like the First World War, it had been at the needless cost of many lives in all the nations involved. Nevertheless, Hugh Schonfield believed that the ideals of a service nation became more necessary in the post war years and he continued to develop the movement (see box). He recognised that change could only be made in small steps by committed groups of people working slowly to change consciousness at the grassroots level.

Frank was of the same view but he was unable to remain actively involved in the movement as the post war years were to be a time of intense activity in nurturing the grassroots of Goosegreen and the nascent organic movement.

****

HUGH J SCHONFIELD (1901-1988)

Hugh Schonfield was a Hebrew Christian who was born in London and became a bible scholar and an expert on the New Testament. Because of the development of fascism and Nazism and the growing threat of war, he decided to launch a Peace Publishing Company and book club in 1935. This was to disseminate the ideas of writers and thinkers to counter this threat and among the people involved in the initiative were J Middleton Murray, H G Wells, George Lansbury, Professor C E M Joad, and Vera Brittain. He founded the Society for the Creation of a Holy Nation in 1940 which later became The Commonwealth of World Citizens with an international following. He was nominated for the Nobel Peace Prize in 1952.

Among a number of books, he wrote, the most controversial was *The Passover Plot* in which he posited that the crucifixion was an attempt by Jesus to divert attention from him to the principles he was advocating and that he had in fact survived the ordeal.

Schonfield's writings and the work of The Commonwealth of World Citizens are continued by the Hugh and Helene Schonfield World Service Trust based in Tuningen, Germany (www.schonfield.org)

****

Chapter 8

The Farmer

As the drive to increase food production got under way in the immediate post war years, the threat to long term soil fertility by the industrialisation of agriculture was epitomised by the 'dust bowls' of the American plains and the tearing up of hedgerows in England to create vast acreages given over to a monoculture supported by the increasing use of nitrogenous fertilisers. The cessation of hostilities had reduced the need for training COs and Frank recognised the need to consolidate the evidence for the benefits that organic husbandry had brought to restoring the health of his farm and its livestock.

In setting out a draft memorandum for the restructuring of the farm company, Frank expressed the need for 'natural farming on the lines of Sir Albert Howard and research to increase food production without recourse to chemical fertilisers'. Indeed, Sir Albert himself had urged Frank to write about his successes at Goosegreen, a task, however, he felt needed the accumulation of more practical evidence before it could be completed. Nevertheless, the need to disseminate the logic of the organic approach was evident to him but it was clear his old journalistic outlets, such as *The Farmer and Stockbreeder* and *Farmers' Weekly*, with their heavy reliance on advertising from fertiliser and veterinary pharmaceutical companies would not take kindly to his rebellious ideas. There was clearly a need for an independent publication devoted to the cause of natural farming and living and Frank conceived the idea of a quarterly magazine, which he initially titled 'Naturally' and for which he even designed a dummy cover with the strap line 'Journal of Natural Farming'.

100 YEARS OF HERBAL MEDICINE

The Armorial Ensigns of
THE NATIONAL INSTITUTE OF MEDICAL HERBALISTS LIMITED
which celebrates its

CENTENARY in the CITY of LONDON

Fitness cover April 1964. The last magazine edited and published by Frank

Throughout the winter of 1945, he worked assiduously in evenings and weekends to solicit advertisers and contributors. He realised, however, that the title needed to have a more agricultural emphasis and so, in the summer of 1946, the first edition of *The Farmer*, 'the journal of natural farming and living' was published as a quarterly at an annual subscription of five shillings post free.

Meanwhile, other initiatives to further the organic cause were under way. In the mid-1940s, Sir Albert Howard took over the Newsletter on Compost, edited by his friend Dr Lionel Picton, one of the authors of the Medical Testament, and relaunched it in February 1946 as a quarterly magazine, *Soil and Health*, to which Frank occasionally contributed. Later in the same year the Soil Association was founded and launched its magazine, *Mother Earth*, edited by Jorian Jenks, which attempted to provide 'serious scientific research and philosophical debate'. (Conford P. *Development of the Organic Network*, p43)

Frank tried to give *The Farmer* a wider appeal by adopting a lighter style with varied content across the perspectives of health and organic husbandry. In the first edition, he set out the mission of the magazine.

'Introducing The Farmer'

We introduce The Farmer, as a modest attempt to publish the truth about soil fertility, animal and human health, and to oppose with all the strength in our power the rapid decline to artificial methods of farming and human living which are boosted by immense vested interests, but which are in fact insidiously ruining the health of our livestock and human community.

The Farmer will derive its policy from the practical experience of the Editor who, on his farm, has practised natural methods of farming, for several years, and seen as a result the remarkable restoration of health to the land and the livestock that live on the farm.

We shall address ourselves to the farmer and townsman alike; to the farmer because we believe he assures the health of the nation, and incidentally his own future survival, in the degree to which he conforms to the laws of nature in the treatment of his land and livestock.

We address ourselves to the townsman, because it is upon the widespread acceptance and practise of the methods of farming and living which we shall advocate in this journal, that his future well-being depends. It is therefore, the duty of every citizen to see to it that he gets an adequate supply of whole food, properly produced from naturally fertilised soil, and from animals which are maintained free of disease in the only way that nature intended in the provision of natural food for man and beast.

We believe that all diseases of crops can be eliminated, but only by the restoration of the world's acres to the vitality of which they have been robbed by the artificial methods of modern commercial exploitation. We believe that all animal and human disease can be eliminated, but only by the consumption of natural fresh food in its unrefined entirety, as it grows in naturally fertilised soil.'

The first edition contained many articles that became regular features, ranging from the musings of the Editor in 'Leaning on the Gate', to reports from 'The Jersey Spring Show and Sale', an article on the value of fever by Dr Cyril

Pink and 'The Farmer's Wife', giving recipes for healthy eating provided by Lorna and others. In his editorial feature Frank speculated on the observation that his cattle seemed more inclined to drink water from streams and ditches than chlorinated tap water in the troughs. He also commented on the low pay of agricultural workers compared to townsmen who 'squandered their wages on drink, tobacco, and dog racing' (which might not have endeared his journal to that section of the readership he was hoping to attract.)

Advertising income was essential to sustaining the venture of course, but Frank was strict about their content: 'Only advertisements of products which can, with confidence, be recommended by the Editor, will be accepted.' Advertisers in the summer 1946 edition included *Health for All*, naturopath Stanley Lief's magazine, Nelson's Homoeopathic Pharmacy, the League Against Cruel Sports, Sir Albert's journal, *Soil and Health* (which didn't carry advertisements), and a small ad for *The World Citizen*, the magazine of Hugh Schonfield's World Service Movement.

The autumn 1946 edition of *The Farmer* (by now costing six shillings and sixpence for an annual subscription) carried a feature announcing the formation of The Soil Association to 'organise education and research into the problems of organic and natural fertilisers, and of methods of cultivating the health of the soil.' The intention was that trial fields comparing organic and conventional plots would be established at New Bells Farm in Haughley, Suffolk, which belonged to Lady Eve Balfour, whose book *The Living Soil* (1943) had aroused the interest of many small scale farmers in the organic ways. In his report Frank expressed a note of dissent by arguing that this work was being well done by pioneering practical farmers in various parts of the world: *Apart from the fact that research work of the kind that is proposed can best be done by individual initiative, the publication of results by an organisation that has had large sums of money at its disposal, will never convince the working farmer like the over the hedge evidence which is actually seen by the neighbours and visitors of the growing band of organic farmers. Let men like Friend Sykes of Chute, Captain Drummond, of Mount Rule IOM, and the Editor of this journal at Goosegreen, get on with their practical farming, leavening the lump of orthodox agriculture under the skill and benevolent guidance of Sir Albert Howard, the man who has discovered and proved natural methods to the satisfaction of all thinking men ...*

(*The Farmer*, Autumn 1946, p29)

This might have seemed like very tart grapes at a time when he had his own financial worries were it not that it echoed the view of Sir Albert himself who did not join the Soil Association because he considered that the Haughley experiment would prove a costly failure. Indeed, he wrote, in this task all concerned will do well to forget everything they have ever learned about chemistry and to bear in mind that the principles underlying composting are biological and not chemical. Although it continued for many years, the Haughley trial cost the Soil Association dearly and ultimately failed to trace a relationship between soil treatment and health. (Conford, 2011, p408) Nevertheless, the Winter 1946 edition of *The Farmer* carried a brief report of the inaugural meeting of the Soil Association, held in October of that year, at which Lord Teviot was elected president and Lady Eve Balfour Organising Secretary, and the headquarters were to be established at her farm at Haughley. Members of the first permanent council included such luminaries of the organic and health reform movement as Laurence Easterbrook, Friend Sykes, Miss Mae Bruce, Lord Portsmouth, Dr Innes Pearce, Richard de la Mare, and Rolf Gardiner. Some of these were to become regular contributors to *The Farmer* and, although the Haughley experiment did not live up to expectations, the Soil Association became one of the most influential organisations in the organic movement and continues to be its principal advocate in the UK.

With the demand for compost grown food increasing it seemed it was time for a more co-ordinated chain of supply to be available and Frank set up a Register of Compost Growers, who would guarantee food grown without any artificial fertilisers. This soon evolved into a Whole Food Society, the formation of which was announced in the Winter 1946 edition of *The Farmer*. (Frank's reference to 'whole food' in his introduction to the first edition of *The Farmer* was probably the first use of the term.)

By this time Derek Randal, who had been a fellow supporter of Hugh Schonfield's Society for the Creation of a Holy Nation, had joined the small community at Goosegreen. He had kept in touch with Frank and Lorna by letter from his theatre touring venues between 1944 and 1946. His wife, Joan, was in poor health but averse to nature cure treatment, as he had hoped that she would go to Stanley Lief's nature cure clinic at Tring. It was clear that the marriage was under strain and by early 1946 they were no longer living together. Once at Goosegreen, he was able to assist Frank with *The Farmer* and they set about establishing the Producer Consumer Whole Food Society Ltd, which was formally constituted under the Industrial and Provident Society Acts in 1948 to:

- promote the production of food by organic methods and to ensure adequate reward for the producer using those methods;
- to facilitate the supply of such whole foods fresh to the consumer;
- to secure the joint participation of producers and consumers in these activities.

The objectives of the Society gained wide support and it attracted many eminent supporters of food reform and natural farming. Once formally constituted, an inaugural meeting was held at Friends' House in London in October 1948. Statements of support were written by Dr Cyril Pink and Robert Henriques, among others, thus linking the health of soil, animals, and humans. Dr Pink wrote: *'Dr Bircher Benner, a great pioneer in this work set up a clinic about 50 years ago in Zurich; it has come into the news lately because Sir Stafford Cripps went there for treatment. The backbone of Dr Bircher Benner's treatment is the right sort of food, and it is the very doctrines he preached that the Whole Food Society is putting into practice. He said that the quality of food was of immense importance, and that it must not be 'cracked up'. He used a German word which has been translated into 'partialised', which means that we take, for example, the grain of wheat and grind it in such a way that the germ, protein, oil and vitamins are all separated from it then we make a loaf of bread of the rest. Parents try to convince their children that this is the Staff of Life, but it is only the Staff of*

Life if it is whole wheat bread. Then we are liable to peel our potatoes and so loose valuable potassium and other salts. There is iodine in apples, but it is contained only in the pips, and if you fail to crunch up the pips then you fail to extract the apple's complete nutritional qualities. Dr Bircher Benner thought 25 years ago that we should eat the apple whole and it was imbecile to peel potatoes, and it was criminal to partialise wheat.'

Frank even made the ambitious suggestion that The Whole Food Society could be an organisation which 'one day removed the need for the colossal National Health Service.' Ironically, it had been the hope of the driving force behind the creation of the NHS, Aneurin Bevan (Minister of Health in Clement Atlee's post war government), that its success would eventually make it redundant, a hope that was not to be fulfilled owing largely to the fact that, far from promoting health – in the way that the Pioneer Health Centre was attempting to – it became a 'disease service' (albeit effective in many ways) but with ever spiralling costs to the national exchequer.

Support and guidance in the establishment of The Whole Food Society came particularly from Sir Albert Howard whose experiences in India and his subsequent books had inspired so many to apply the 'rule of return' to their agricultural and horticultural endeavours. He assisted Frank in drawing up the rules and constitution of the WFS and was to have been its first president, when the whole organic world was shaken by the news of his death in October 1947 at the age of 73.

Frank devoted more than half the winter 1947 issue of *The Farmer* to tributes from Sir Albert's many friends and followers including Friend Sykes, Doris Grant, J I Rodale, (the American organic advocate and publisher), The Earl of Portsmouth, Dr Cyril Pink, Dr Lionel Picton, Lady Eve Balfour, and F C King. As Frank wrote in his 'Leaning on the Gate' editorial: *Few men have done more to ensure the survival of humanity than Sir Albert Howard, though the people are but vaguely aware of the debt they owe this great man.*

He went on reiterate Sir Albert's antipathy to the calls for orthodox statistical proof by the chemical fertiliser lobby.' *"If we try to prove our case statistically, we shall be playing their game" he said. "They want us to waste our slender resources on experiments that will take at least 50 years, during which time they can go on selling their 'devil's dust' on the pretext that the compost people still have not finished their experiments."*

And it was this emphasis by Sir Albert on the importance of empiricism and learning from observation of nature that was the recurring theme of most of the tributes.

In the same edition of *The Farmer*, Frank announced the formation of the Albert Howard Institute of Organic Husbandry, to which Lady Howard had given her approval and support. As the announcement stated 'the greatest need at the moment in the organic gardening and farming movement is for the provision of training facilities and the opportunity for experiencing composting and other methods of natural farming. The first aim, therefore, will be to meet this need by arranging simple residential courses in the Indore system of composting originated by Sir Albert Howard.'

So, it was that the seed was sown for the series of weekend courses that were held at Goosegreen from 1949 onwards, but it was felt that more farms and gardens were needed for the initiative and a wider body, known as the Albert Howard Foundation, was set up. The president was Lady Howard and Frank became chairman.

It soon became apparent that some form of quality control was necessary to counter the tendency of some suppliers to advertise their produce as 'organically grown' or 'free from chemicals' and the Autumn 1946 edition of *The Farmer* had announced the intention to issue a compost certificate of registration as a grower of compost grown produce. This evolved into The Whole Food Society's idea of a Whole Food Mark. The committee defined whole food as: 'mature produce of field, orchard, or garden without subtraction, addition or alteration, grown from seed without chemical dressing in fertile soil manured solely with animal and vegetable wastes, and compost therefrom and ground raw rock and without chemical manures, sprays, or insecticides.'

Because the Whole Food Society had objectives in common with the Soil Association, Derek Randal and Frank held meetings with Lady Eve Balfour to arrange for their Whole Food Bulletin to be distributed to members of the association. They also decided to launch a competition for the design of a Whole Food Mark.

The notion of a Mark, first conceived in 1946, underwent an elephantine gestation. A design eventually appeared and as the idea gained wide support, the Soil Association convened a series of meetings in early 1951 at which representatives of the WFS, the Albert Howard Foundation, the Biodynamic Agricultural Association, Men of the Trees (represented by its founder, Richard St Barbe Baker) and representatives of growers, to discuss the Mark and its administration. While there was general consensus on the need for a Mark there was much debate about how it could be administered. With their interests and resources ranging widely from the stringent criteria of the Biodynamic group to the Men of the Trees, dedicated to the conservation of woodlands and forests, none was ideally equipped to undertake the task. The hope was that the WFS, having originated the idea, might be able to do so but this might have necessitated it to reconstruct its objectives and, in any case, it was at this time in a financially precarious position. The initiative to create an organic benchmark shrivelled in the womb and it was not until the 1960s that the Soil Association revived the idea and established its organic mark.

By 1948 *The Farmer* had gained a worldwide if numerically modest readership. Frank had come to an arrangement with J I Rodale, an eminent American publisher, writer and organic farmer, for reciprocal distribution of his magazine *Organic Gardening*, and *The Farmer* in their respective countries. F C King, who ran a successful organic market garden in Kendall, Westmorland, for many years, wrote in *The Farmer*, Autumn 1948 edition, about his methods of gardening without digging to launch a regular gardening section in the magazine. Frank had also experimented with making the plough redundant at Goosegreen. In the same edition of *The Farmer* he wrote a lengthy article about his experience which, although challenging at first on account of the weeds, he was able, within a year or two, to turn them to advantage with the use of the disc harrow. The key to success for both F C King and

117

Frank lay in the application of Sir Albert Howard's principals of composting and mulching. As Frank observed: 'Nature does not plough; she employs the earthworm and soil bacteria, together with deeply penetrating roots to do her work.'

Breaking up the surface soil with the disc harrow or chain harrow enabled him to sow in unploughed fields and yield healthy crops, nourished by the minerals drawn from the subsoil by deep rooting 'weeds'.

The Farmer stand at an agricultural show

The following year was one of even more intense activity to consolidate the cause of organic husbandry and organic ideals. *The Farmer* took a stand at the major agricultural shows, including the Bath and West Show at Bristol, the Royal Agricultural Show at Shrewsbury, and the Dairy Show at the Olympia Exhibition Centre in London, at which readers could meet contributors to the journal and pick their brains on specialised aspects of organic farming and gardening. Subsequent editions of *The Farmer* carried a full page of caricatures, drawn by the cartoonist Fred May, of the leading figures in agriculture seen at the shows, including 'your own Editor, F Newman Turner'. Fred May also sketched a panel of experts at a Food and Farming Any Questions? held on October 25th 1950, at the Kingsway Hall, London.

Food & Farming Any Questions, 1950. (Cartoon by Fred May for The Farmer)

The Food and Farming Any Questions? was sponsored by the Whole Food Society and had been many months in the planning. Frank and Derek were keen that the panel should represent the full spectrum of opinion in farming and health and they secured the participation of Ralph Wightman, a well-known farmer and broadcaster, and Dr G E Breen, Editor of the Medical Press, while Frank and Robert Henriques were there as Nature's advocates. The Question Master was Freddie Grisewood, who, for many years, presented the long running BBC radio programme Any Questions? A lively but cordial debate ensued on a wide range of topics including the UK policy of slaughter of cattle with foot and mouth disease. Wightman argued that this was necessary to contain the disease and could not countenance trials in which naturally reared animals could be mixed with infected herds to test their immunity which Frank had suggested. He argued that the disease is no more than a severe form of bovine influenza and that the slaughter policy made about as much sense as slaughtering human victims of the flu. Freddie Grisewood remarked, 'I have to agree with Newman Turner. I wanted to slaughter two fellow passengers in my railway compartment on the way here!'

The Farmer 10th Birthday Luncheon

That a magazine with a niche, if growing, readership should have survived ten years was a considerable achievement. Frank had invited both bouquets and brickbats from people across the spectrum of opinions within agriculture and health and many of these were published in the Spring 1956 edition of *The Farmer*. Brickbats were few (Ralph Wightman: 'I think my criticism is that you overstate a case and seldom get away from the one subject') while bouquets were generous and constructive from around the world. Responses from leading organic and health reform advocates which included Dr Ralph Bircher, J.I. Rodale, Lady Eve Balfour, Doris Grant, Victor Bonham Carter, Dr Wm.A. Albrecht, and Lawrence D. Hills, were supportive.

On 28th May, 1956, a 10th Birthday Luncheon was held at the de Vere Hotel, in Kensington, London, attended by about thirty readers and contributors to *The Farmer*. A four course meal was followed by an Any Questions on food, health, and farming which were discussed by a panel consisting of Prof V.H. Mottram (former professor of physiology at London University), Dr C.V. Pink, Fyfe Robertson, Doris Grant, Lawrence D. Hills, Peter D. Turner (no relation, writer and animal welfare campaigner).

Proposing the toast of *The Farmer* over lunch, Dr Pink said: "I think I have been chosen for this really nice job because I have known it for so long; indeed, I really did some of the ante natal work for *The Farmer*. But I think the most important part I played was in introducing Newman Turner to Sir Albert Howard. They hadn't met before, and as Sir Albert was a neighbour of ours we arranged for them to meet at our home. It was a very fruitful meeting and rather extraordinary in some ways – I think they started talking about 7 o'clock in the evening. I got tired somewhere near midnight and asked if I could go to sleep! I remember Lady Howard rang up once or twice to ask when her husband was coming home! But still they continued."

Responding to the toast, Frank explained something of the struggles and sacrifices of his family. All royalties from his books had gone into keeping *The Farmer* alive. He was also obliged to reveal the contents of a letter from the owners of the Ferne estate that was sent to the hotel giving notice to cease publication from the farm. (See chapter 13, Ferne Farm)

Peter D. Turner proposed the toast to the readers and guests and said: "The ideal reader of *The Farmer* is prepared to demonstrate …that there is a unity between the truly useful, and the truly scientific, and the truly humane. To me that is the great ideal for which *The Farmer* stands"

Doris Grant, responding, spoke of the chemical dragon which is breathing its foul breath over the land, over our food, invading our homes and our farms in many different disguises – always parading as a friend of man, as a household pet, a farm pet, so its dangerous character is completely unsuspected by the majority of its victims. She thanked *The Farmer* for taking on the role of St George and fighting the dragon so efficiently.

Chapter 9

The Tale of Tombreen

Behind the public persona of the publishing and the promotion of the organic ethos lay the practicalities of running the farm and the demands of a pedigree Jersey herd that Frank had been building since 1943. Sir Albert Howard had urged Frank to purchase the farm outright pointing out that he should reap the benefits of the fertility he had created rather than building it for an absent landlord.

Following a visit to Goosegreen in 1946, Sir Albert wrote to Frank on a Soil and Health letterhead reporting that he had immediately written to Richard de la Mare, the agricultural editor at Faber and Faber, and to Captain George Drummond suggesting that his family bank might consider a mortgage for Frank if he decided to purchase Goosegreen.

Captain George H. Drummond was a landowner and a member of a Scottish banking family who farmed organically on the Isle of Man. As a reader of *The Farmer*, he was keen on the suggestion that Frank should talk to the farmers on the island. In August 1946, he had purchased a 500-acre estate 65 miles south of Dublin, near the small town of Carnew in Co. Wicklow, Eire. Just as Goosegreen had been, Tombreen was rather run down and Drummond wished to farm it organically as he did his farm at Mount Rule, IOM. He believed that Frank might be the person to manage the Tombreen estate and supervise another farm he had at Courtown some thirty miles to the north, in Co Kildare. Despite his commitments at Goosegreen, Frank, for his part was enthused by the opportunity of putting the organic experiment to the test on larger scale, especially with the prospect that it would be financed by someone of Drummond's apparent wealth. Perhaps he was being rather optimistic for the tale of his Tombreen adventure turned out to be a series of misunderstandings and over commitments.

He met Captain Drummond at the Savoy Hotel in London on August 20th 1946 to discuss terms, after which Frank wrote to Drummond suggesting that he would commence supervision of Tombreen as soon as a suitable man to look after Goosegreen could be arranged. He went on to suggest "some form of partnership rather than I should be employed simply as your manager. I feel sure you will appreciate, in view of my position as Editor of The Farmer, the publication of my book and other factors, the importance of this distinction in my position." He also drew up a Memorandum of Undertaking between the two of them regarding 'the farming of Tombreen and adjacent lands' by which Drummond would put up the cash on a five percent basis and Frank was to receive a salary of £750 per annum 'plus use of the house, light, milk, butter, potatoes, and use of furniture taken over from Martinson (the vendor) until it can be replaced – also 25% of profits.'

Although these terms don't seem to have been agreed, Frank started commuting between Tombreen and Goosegreen and he wrote to Kenneth Hollowell, by now his family solicitor, to say that he was 'starting work on reclamation by natural methods of a 500 acre worn out farm in partnership with a friend'. Hollowell, meanwhile, was engaged in conveyancing Frank's purchase of Goosegreen Farm from Goosegreen Farm Ltd (from whom he had leased it) for an agreed price of £10,400. The purchase was supported by a loan of £5,000 from Captain Drummond (by way of debentures in F. Newman Turner Ltd) and another from an S G Hannam for £8,000 which provided him with some working capital in addition to the purchase price.

Drummond, however, was not disposed to the idea of a company or partnership for farming Tombreen. As he wrote in May 1947:*I do not understand what you require re our association of farming of Tombreen. Neither a company nor a partnership is possible, the former for the expense and the latter because you have no capital. Nothing can alter the main facts re our undertaking.*

To which Frank replied from Tombreen:

"I'm a little disturbed about your change of plan regarding partnership as it was never my intention to come here as a manager and this I stated clearly from the start. I was confident that you had agreed to this, and at our Savoy Hotel meeting to agree terms you said that we could draw up a partnership without any investment on my part and that I should have the opportunity of investing capital and increasing my proportion of the partnership at a later date."

Nevertheless, early in the harsh winter of 1947, Frank, Lorna, and we two boys had made the journey through Wales by car to take the ferry from Fishguard to Rosslaire on the east coast of Ireland and drove north from there to Carnew, at the southern tip of Co. Wicklow, to move into Tombreen House. Frank arranged for his brother, Kenneth, to manage Goosegreen and in February 1947 he came down from the Turner family farm in Yorkshire to live in the farmhouse with his wife Margaret and their infant son, Timothy.

Tombreen House, Eire, 1947

Tombreen was a Georgian manor house, situated a mile or so outside Carnew in gentle rolling countryside. It had been part of the Lord Fitzwilliam estate. The house was in good repair and overlooked a meadow which sloped gently down to a peat bog and a stream in front of a wood. The stables and outhouses were arranged around a quadrangle at the back of the house and there was a room where the farm labourers could take tea breaks and where they introduced me, at the age of seven, to cigarettes which helped to put me off smoking for the rest of my life! Some rewiring and minor renovations were required in the house and furniture had to be acquired as Frank and Lorna had decided not to sell the furniture at Goosegreen which, in any case, was needed there. In September, while Lorna was on a visit to Cornwall with the boys, Frank viewed some antique furniture and Persian rugs being offered by Lady Nelson, a fellow Jersey breeder in Eire, who needed to raise cash. They eventually bought several items of limed oak including an escritoire that had belonged to William III during the Irish Occupation. This was a large cabinet with a fold down writing desk that revealed numerous drawers, a number of which had concealed compartments.

While reviving the farmland of Tombreen in what was a climatically challenging summer in Co. Wicklow, Frank was continuing to edit *The Farmer*, with the help of Derek Randal back at Goosegreen, and to supervise the farm, assisted by his brother, Kenneth. He returned to Goosegreen every two or three months for meetings with API to formalise debentures for F Newman Turner Ltd and completion of the purchase from the directors of Goosegreen Farm Ltd, which was eventually wound up. Kenneth Hollowell had written to report a delay in completion of the purchase owing to some confusion with a series of mortgages on the farm taken out in 1909 by the then owner, Thomas Clarke. (It seems the financial drain of Goosegreen on the incumbents had a strong historical precedent!) Once the matter was resolved, Hollowell was finally able to report completion of the purchase on the 25th July, just beating the deadline of the 1st August when new budget provisions were to come into force doubling the stamp duty on all deeds. As it was Hollowell had racked up considerable fees himself in sorting out all the legal complexities and, in a letter to API, Frank expressed his shock at the cost of the purchase "It leaves us with no margin at all. It looks as if we shall have to get on with selling some of the younger stock quickly so we shall have a little working margin. We had planned to do this, as I think we should take advantage of the high prices ruling for pedigree stock that is reaching maturity." (It is not clear what became of the surplus capital raised by the mortgage and loan) It had been his intention to export a bull and six heifers to Tombreen to build up the pedigree stock there. Kenneth Turner had arranged for them to be placed in quarantine in Liverpool prior to shipment to Dublin docks but this was later cancelled as Frank had purchased a bull 'of good breeding' from Lady Nelson in Ireland.

Frank was increasingly in demand as a speaker and made more appearances on regional radio stations. In his letter to Lorna, in Cornwall, he wrote:

It is now certain that I shall not return until September 30th, getting back to Goosegreen on October 1st. Should I go straight on to the Reading Show and Sale on the 2nd or should I come to Goosegreen on the 1st and go on to Reading on the 2nd. Of course, it may be wise to miss the Show and Sale but if it can be fitted in I would like to do it. I have to speak at Bath on October the 4th, Swindon on the 7th and Bures (Suffolk) on the 8th, back home on the 9th and to Bristol on the 11th. Would you like to come back to Goosegreen during all this, or stay at Corbor until it is over and meet me at Goosegreen or let me come down to Corbor on the 12th?

And then, in a rare acknowledgement of the punishing schedule he was inflicting on himself, he wrote: *I am coming to the conclusion that I am rather foolish to take on all these lectures. They are something of a tie to me and their value is doubtful in view of all the other things that I have on hand ... after all, I think Sir Albert was right in the beginning of our negotiations about Tombreen, and we seem to have forgotten his valuable advice, when he said 'it doesn't matter what you do so long as you get that book written; that is your most important task until it is published. Now I think he was right and my best plan is probably to give that first place and get the book finished at Tombreen this winter if it is at all possible.*

Frank also mentioned the likelihood of the farm opposite Tombreen being bought by an English major and his youngish wife who had a large family. *If they are at all approachable they should provide company for you and the children and possibly share a governess. I have not, therefore, pressed George to buy the place in front of this man, for I think it is all to the good to have more English people around us here.*

By now, Kenneth Turner was keen to return to Yorkshire, so Frank needed to interview candidates for the post of a farm manager to replace him. No one suitable seems to have been found so he arranged, provisionally, for Tony Capozzoli and his wife to live in one part of the farmhouse at Goosegreen, while Derek and his wife Joan (who had re-joined him for a short time) lived at the other end.

Frank went ahead with improvements to Tombreen both structurally and agriculturally. He put in place renovations to the farm cottages, and to improve the herd, purchased heifers and that nice bull, from Lady Nelson, for 200 guineas which, he said, 'should return that in no time with his progeny as he has plenty of milk and butterfat behind him. 'Throughout the summer, he reported regularly to Drummond on plans for the cottages, the progress of hay making aided by a few days of fine weather, and further items of expenditure and progress with the decoration of Tombreen. He also announced that 'I am thinking of giving the men the option of a half day holiday or five shillings a week over the statutory 50 shillings in addition to Sunday off each week (stock men of course work Sundays). In addition, after harvest I shall give them each a week's holiday with pay. I feel sure you will approve.'

But, as autumn approached, Frank's peripatetic life was already beginning to rankle with Drummond, who was probably used to people dancing to his tune. Although many of his letters to Frank were handwritten (or, to be more accurate, dashed off, as they are difficult to decipher), his estates were managed by an agent, T L Vondy, and he had employed a purveyor of tripods, Alexander Proctor, as an agricultural consultant to report on the state of Tombreen before he purchased it.

On 5th September, he dashed off another letter: *Will you please stop all building of cottages etc. and not order anything more until I have seen you. The time has come when I am not prepared to go into any further expenditure unless it is absolutely necessary, and I propose to consolidate whatever the position is at which we have arrived. I think that prices will go up until everything crashes and when that happens will be the time to build. I strongly advise you to sell the farm in England. You can now sell out at the top and I should certainly play for safety and if you can get out without loss I should certainly do so. I hope you will seriously go into this question as it is obvious you ought to make sure of being able to put your 25% into Tombreen.*

Frank replied that he would need to discuss the future of Goosegreen with Lorna and his brother when he was next over there. He added a request to use turf for fuel: *The house is terribly damp – both main living rooms show wet creeping up the walls halfway and the paper is thick with mould in one corner. This means that fires must be kept going in the winter and if turf is not included in our agreement I shall be tempted to strip the farm of its little remaining timber. I feel sure in the circumstances that you will allow the use of turf in the farmhouse. Actually, most agreements of this kind do include the use of fuel of all kinds.* This rather contradicted the report from Proctor that the manor house was in good repair.

Drummond, meanwhile had transferred ownership of Tombreen to a company he had set up called Courtown Estates and delegated his agent, Vondy, to conduct dealings with Frank. These included an implication that Frank's management of the farm at Tombreen had not been satisfactory and that he might consider returning to Goosegreen. But by now Frank had committed himself to the challenge of the Tombreen restoration. He wrote again to Drummond:

19th Oct 194. I have thought over and discussed with my wife the suggestions put forward by Mr Vondy on your behalf and we feel that having gone so far in establishing ourselves in Tombreen and cleared off most of our commitments in England it would be extremely difficult to reverse the process. We have installed a business manager for the farm and The Farmer at Goosegreen, and arranged for the place to be carried on in my absence; we have moved everything over here except the furniture we intend bringing and some crockery and smaller things all of which are packed ready for despatch and my wife is thankful to have got through the long and tiring practice of packing and listing everything for removal. I could not ask her to go through all that again, in reverse at any rate not without a considerable interval to enable her to recover her breath. I have resigned my position as Chairman of the Jersey Breeders Club and cut out lectures for the next six months and refused to take on any new ones. So that, after the Dairy Show, it is not likely that I shall have to go more often than quarterly to get out The Farmer. I'm even making enquiries about getting The Farmer published over here as paper restrictions in England are preventing me from increasing circulation .I would like to suggest therefore, that we continue for the next 12 months during which time you will be satisfied that Tombreen is my main interest in life, at least until I have made it into the sort of farm that will create organic farming interest such as we have never seen before. I'm sure you must appreciate that the last 12 months have been a difficult transitional period. It was not easy to pack in everything in England at once. I told you I could not settle here for 6 or 9 months; it has been longer than that but I had no idea how much there was to clear up. I would not have gone through the transfer had I not felt that Tombreen offered a great opportunity to demonstrate to the world what could be done to a worn out farm by organic means entirely, and at the same time to show a handsome return on capital outlay. And for me at any rate, the first year has been most encouraging. Next year will begin to show results.

Soon after this Vondy prepared a report for Captain Drummond which was critical of Frank's management of

Tombreen. He had already suggested that phosphates should be used on the land to obtain quicker results but Frank pointed out to Drummond that fresh evidence from France had shown that the reason slag and potash cause disease was because they destroy trace elements in the soil that are essential to health. Frank maintained cordial correspondence with Vondy but Drummond was becoming increasingly irritated: *"You have never written to me except when we have written to you. You have never let us know the dates you were away in spite of my repeatedly asking you to let me know and I think I wrote you and telephoned you. It is bad enough not to know the date you are going and it is even worse still not knowing the date of your return. The last time I went to Tombreen you had arranged to be there but without letting one know you suddenly came a day later. This to me was the last straw especially, after I had seen the condition of the cattle, building and machines and that nothing had been done to enable these to be put under cover."*

Having committed themselves to the Tombreen project, Frank and Lorna were determined to hold out in spite of the precariousness of their position. The family spent Christmas at Tombreen and, with an eye to the future, Frank responded to an advertiser in The Irish Times offering her 'an interesting post' as a secretary/governess: 'The work would consist of part time clerical work – shorthand, typing, correspondence, filing etc., in connection with my publication The Farmer and my farm here in Ireland; and part time as governess to our two boys Roger, aged nearly eight and Giles aged 2 ½ years. The older boy would need to be given simple lessons daily and both boys would need to be amused and assisted in their occupations out of doors. They have a small pony and various dogs. We should also wish you to take complete charge of the children when my wife is out. "This is a pleasant country house, two miles from Carnew, where there is a predominantly protestant township. We would provide you with a private bed sitting room which you could use for all or some of your meals as you wish and we should have no objection to your small dog provided you would look after any mess he may make, though no doubt he or she is house trained!"

The wage offered was £2.00 per week plus full board and lodging.

Drummond, however, seemed determined to pull the plug on the whole venture and in February 1948, AL Whiteside, the accountant to Courtown Estates wrote to confirm that the farm would be put up for auction on 27th April followed by a dispersal sale on 8th May with vacant possession of the farm on 1st June. "Would you therefore accept this letter as official intimation that your services will be terminated on 31st May 1948, and that you will give up vacant possession of the house at Tombreen by that date."

Further correspondence ensued regarding the possibility of Frank selling Goosegreen to be able to purchase Tombreen, as Drummond had suggested. There were also the loans on Goosegreen – including that of Drummond's Bank– to be considered, and it seems that interest payments on these were falling into arrears. It was not until September, however, that Frank wrote to him to say that he would ask auctioneers to proceed with negotiations for a possible sale of Goosegreen to Oxford University for £15,000, adding that he was selling stock as quickly as possible in order to raise the money required to pay off the mortgages. He went on to write: *I can assure you no one regards this matter with more urgency than I for it is a source of perpetual worry, both to my wife and to me, and we wish to be in a position to get on with our work with a little less anxiety as soon as it can be arranged. 'I'm sorry I seem to be less than my age in these matters. I suppose there are times when we all show signs of childishness, but hope it will not be necessary for us to indulge in personal innuendos about our respective failings in clearing up our business together.*

The family returned to Somerset in the summer of 1948, as it was clear they did not have a future in Ireland. There was ongoing correspondence with Courtown Estates to clear up residual financial queries and with the new owner of Tombreen regarding the shipping of the furniture – including many of the antique items they had purchased while living there – as well as two ponies, all of which required export licences before they could be sent to Goosegreen. It was to be another couple of years before F Newman Turner Ltd's indebtedness to Captain Drummond would be discharged by way of securing an alternative loan from the Agricultural Mortgage Corporation secured on the farm.

They did not sell Goosegreen. There was much to concentrate on with *The Farmer* – now gaining an international readership – the Jersey herd, the completion of the book, the weekend courses, and a stream of visitors keen to learn more about the practicalities of organic husbandry, so the next few years were ones of intense activity.

Captain George H Drummond (3 March 1883-12 Oct 1963)

Although the environmental concerns of most followers of the organic movement would place them to the left of the political spectrum there were many who were more right-wing in their beliefs. Among those at the far right end of the spectrum was Captain George Drummond, a descendant of the Scottish banking family, Drummond's Bank, founded in 1717.

Drummond was believed to be a Nazi sympathiser and was active in the British Union of Fascists, founded by Oswald Mosley in 1932. Drummond was the president of the Northamptonshire branch of the BUF when he lived at Pitsford Hall, which he had purchased in the 1920s. He is believed to have had a Swastika emblazoned on the bottom of the hall's swimming pool. A friend of the Royal family, he entertained the Prince of Wales (later King Edward VIII) and his brother, the Duke of York (later King George VI) who were regular visitors.

When Drummond was caught with a high frequency radio – banned at the time – and found to have chopped down some trees to obtain a better view of a nearby airfield, officers of the Intelligence Agency MI5 had him interned on the Isle of Man in 1940 where he lived on another family estate at Mount Rule.

Chapter 10

Cattle Matters

The joy of Jerseys

With the seasonal fluctuations of the farming year, a pivotal part of any mixed farm is the dairy herd. It is an essential provider of regular cash flow when income from crops is susceptible to the vagaries of the weather. Frank had spent his childhood among cows. He had milked his first cow at the age of five and by the age of twelve, was regularly milking a dozen cows twice a day. Having cared for the cattle in several jobs after graduating with his dairying diploma from Auchenchyle School of Dairying, attached to Glasgow University, and then as an advisor for a cattle feed company in the 1930s, he had adequate experience to meet the demands of managing the dairy herd at Goosegreen.

They were considerable. Frank wrote in the Autumn 1945 edition of *The Countryman*: *When, three years ago, I took over the farm of which I had been manager, with everything as it stood, I knew the risks. Most of the fields had not been ploughed for generations. The mixed cross bred herd of Dairy Shorthorns and Friesians had been riddled with abortion, tuberculosis, and sterility. The first tuberculin test showed seventeen reactors out of a herd of sixty-five, all the reactors being cows wintered indoors in enclosed but well ventilated buildings; not one of the cows housed in open backed, exposed sheds reacted, nor had any of the younger animals which were wintered out or kept in open shelters.*

It was a situation which impressed upon him the need to adopt a policy of cattle rearing that brought them closer to nature. The concentrated cattle cake that he had been paid to persuade his customers to use when he had worked for Farm Industries in the thirties, had to be phased out, effecting a not inconsiderable saving. He began to out winter the cattle and ensured a steady supply of fodder with hay and silage when grazing was poor. In the summer, the herd fed on mixed herbal leys in which he included garlic, and it was these which were the basis of his strategy to restore the health of the cattle, the deeper rooting plants drawing up essential minerals and trace elements from the sub soil. The ley contained as wide a variety of herbs as possible and the garlic, a natural cleanser, did not taint the milk when mixed with them.

Frank also made the decision to switch from the heavier breeds which constituted the herd he had taken over. As many of them were cross bred, there would be advantages to having a pedigree line. It was not just for this reason that he settled on Jerseys. *It was the purchase of two cheap first class heifers for the house which demonstrated to me the amazing ability of these little animals to convert food into milk at remarkably low cost.*

(*Herdsmanship* p172)

At that time, Jerseys were a hardy and adaptable breed, Frank believed, because they had not suffered exploitative methods of management to extract excessive yields but were reared in a balanced system of care. Jersey breeders had fed their cows naturally, often not being subject to the commercial incentive to produce high milk yields, giving them an inheritance of health and a sound constitution.

Although they do not produce the volume of milk of the heavier breeds, Jerseys do not convert their food to body fat but rather to butter fat yield, a quality Frank attributed to the extensive use of seaweed to manure the soil on the island of Jersey from which they originated. In his book *Herdsmanship*, published in 1952, (and which he dedicated to 'The Jersey cow which combines beauty with efficiency.') Frank was able to demonstrate that the cost per gallon of maintaining his Jerseys was more economical than that for the other breeds in the herd (in this case Shorthorn and Shorthorn Friesian cross breeds.)

Weekend Course students compacting the silage clamp,1949

Frank's cattle lived almost entirely out of doors and they grew shaggy protective coats which retained body heat in winter, so effectively that, as he noted in *Herdsmanship*, *in extremely frosty weather they often came in for milking with white hoar frost and icicles in their hair.* (*Herdsmanship* p174) The silage clamp (or stack), which had been well compacted by the students at the weekend courses or with a tractor, were often situated somewhere in the farmyard, so the silage had to be cut and spread in the field. Frank therefore devised a system whereby the cattle could self-feed from clamps built in the field.

A table ledge was cut along one vertical side of the clamp from which the cows could pull out the silage as they needed it. The quantity of silage the cows could take was controlled by changing the angle of the cut, the steeper the angle of the feeding face, the less they could pull out. (See diagram from *Fertility Pastures*) Although the cows could line up at the long side of the silage clamp, there were invariably two or three 'boss cows' who would barge in (this was before de-horning became a regular practice) then sit and chew in the straw laid at the foot of the clamp to keep the mud to a minimum. This meant having to lay more straw a little distance from the clamp to encourage the bullies to allow the timider cows and heifers to get a turn at the table.

In the wet winter months, mud was a problem, not just at the silage clamp but in the gateways as fifty or sixty cattle were brought through them twice a day for milking. Their udders became caked with mud which had to hosed off and washed before they could be milked. The shorter legged ideal show cow was particularly prone to this. So, Frank hit on the idea of a brassiere for cows. He made a prototype out of plastic with webbing straps, and although a photograph of the cow which modelled it did appear in one of the red topped tabloid newspapers (pre dating the 'Page Three Girl' by many years!), it never became a practical commercial proposition.

Frank with Polden Haughty Hetty at Ferne Farm, 1953

For the gourmet cow – and most Jerseys are – silage and kale are the menus of choice but hay could be a good staple of the diet if harvested using the tripod system. Tripods were quite widely used in Scottish crofting and in Scandinavia and enabled grass to be cut earlier – when it was more nutritious

– and stored in the field, well into the winter if necessary. Labour intensive though it was, the tripod system of storing hay removed one significant item from the litany of weather related worries for the average farmer: *Before I started the weatherproof hay making ten years ago, as each June came around, my life became a perpetual worry about the weather, and my hair began to go rapidly greyer every year. Now I can make hay when the grass is at its best; and what is more, it is hay with twenty percent protein content as green as the best dried grass and with a higher food value. Each year now instead of greyer hair, I have greener hay!*

(*Fertility Pastures* new edition p43)

****

Tripod Hay Making

Seven to eight foot straight larch or Douglas fir poles are wired together at one end in threes so that, when erected, they form a tripod. A wooden A frame is placed at the outer corner of each tripod to permit ventilation and a triangle of wire is placed around the tripod at about 2 ½ and 5 feet above the ground.

Grass that is freshly mown and followed with a tedder, is allowed to lay on the field for 24-hours then placed over the frames and wires, being careful to leave the centre of the tripod open. More grass is draped over the top to form a dome which is tied over the top and sides with twine to prevent wind damage. Well-built tripods can be left out in all weathers until the cows are given access to them or the hay is brought in for baling.

****

One of the advantages of a pedigree herd was a certainty in the transmission of ancestry which Frank considered made for better milk yields. As the herd became exclusively Jersey, they were registered as the Polden herd (in reference to the Polden Hills which bordered Goosegreen) and each cow was named and registered with the English Jersey Cattle Society (EJCS). As is the case with racehorses, some imagination was required with the choice of names. Perhaps the character of the heifer calf had something to do with the name but Polden Haughty Hetty, born in October 1944, became a most docile cow, averaging over five percent butterfat yield and earning a certificate of merit from the EJCS. Polden Miss Mannin was born on the 3rd November 1949, just over two months after the author and novelist Ethel Mannin had visited Goosegreen with her husband Reginald Reynolds, also a writer.

Visiting family at Brockholes Farm in the Jowett, circa 1953. L-R Frank, Kenneth, Geoffrey, Philip and their mother, Mary, with Lorna, Giles, and Adam

Polden Chocolate Cake, born in March 1951, was named for the chocolate cake Lorna had baked to celebrate her birth and, perhaps living up to the richness of her name, went on to win a Gold Medal Certificate for a 6.1 percent butterfat yield at her third lactation. Frank and Lorna's friendship with Dr Cyril Pink and his wife Marguerite and the birth of their second and third sons, Giles and Adam, were marked at the naming of Polden Stonefield Baby in 1951 for both Giles and Adam had been born at Dr Pink's maternity home, Stonefield.

The reputation of a pedigree herd did not just depend on milk and butterfat yield. Their success at agricultural shows added kudos to their credentials. Frank entered several of his cows – and his main breed bull, Longmore Mogullas Top Sergente (cattle he had brought in when establishing his herd retained their original registration name) – in many of the agricultural shows that took place each summer throughout the West Country and they accumulated a good collection of prize winners rosettes.

The Polden Jersey herd at Goosegreen, circa 1950 with Haughty
Hetty front L (Photo: Douglas Allen)

Preparation for the shows required a considerable
investment of time in training both cattle and herdsmen and
needed to begin six weeks before a show. Having selected the
cows for showing and, ideally, ensured that they had calved a
month or two before showing when they would be at their
best, the shaggy winter coat needed to be stripped. A rug
might be placed over the cow to raise the temperature and
bring forward the shedding of the winter coat. Then a daily
grooming was necessary and any dung scraped off with a
curry comb. Frank also recommended the addition of a small
amount of seaweed meal to the milking mash to give lustre to
the coat.

Heifers needed to be haltered and accustomed to being led
before they were a year old and the herdsmen also needed
coaching in showing off the cows to their best advantage, just

as models on the catwalk must show off their designers' creations. Before the show, the cow or bull was given a further wash and shampoo, and the horns were scraped and treated with emery paper prior to a coat of varnish or linseed oil to give a final gloss. Rough hair around the root of the tails was clipped and the tail switch was plaited and covered in sacking to keep urine and dung off until shortly before entering the ring. The horns may have been the crowning glory, but the wavy tail switch of the show ready cow gave her that final touch of glamour.

Some Jersey prize winners at Goosegreen

All the effort of preparation was worth it. There were rosettes galore in agricultural shows all over the West Country, including the Bath & West Show, which ranked alongside the Royal Agricultural Show and the Dairy Show for prestige in the UK agricultural calendar. Top Sergente also had his share of the glory, leading the grand parade as best bull in show at the Dorchester Show in 1949. Equipped with such expertise in the finer points of the Jersey cow Frank eventually became a regular judge for the EJCS at many agricultural shows throughout the west.

There were many features to be considered for a prize winning Jersey cow from the nostrils (high and open), the back (straight from the withers to the setting of the tail), wide hips (fine in the bone), the barrel (deep, broad, and long, denoting good capacity), to the udder (well-balanced in line with the belly, with uniform teats).

These were technical features that were essential in a good Jersey cow but Frank also liked to look them in the eye: *'The eyes should be bright and intelligent. If you can't get a clear colourful reflection of yourself in the cow's eyes she can't be in good health. A dull eye is the window of a sour stomach and a sad heart; pass it by! I have found that an intelligent, although not necessarily a pretty face, denotes the ability to produce efficiently. I have never known a cow which is an efficient milk producer to have an unintelligent face, which may sound a tall story to the man who hasn't spent as long as I have looking cows in the face and who may consider all cows' faces potentially dumb anyhow.*

(*Herdsmanship* p35)

Frank attributed the success of his cattle in the show ring above all to building their health by feeding them on the pastures of organically grown deep rooting plants that provided minerals and trace elements often lacking in commercial cattle food. Any sick animals were treated using nature cure principles. He wrote in the forward to his booklet *Cure your own Cattle* published in 1950 under *The Farmer* imprint: *I left university with the deep bewilderment about animal diseases, which I imagine is common to all agricultural and veterinary students. The only certain thing about animal diseases seemed to be man's inability to prevent or cure them. It was not until I had experienced these diseases in my own herd and started at the beginning in my attempt to eliminate and prevent them, instead of accepting the diseases and treating them as inevitable, that I discovered the root cause of most of them. Until, in fact, I discovered that there is only one disease of animals and its name is man! The solution was then simple. If I could get the animals back to a life as nearly as economically practicable to what it was before man perverted them to his own use, and provide them as fully as possible with all the requirements of health available under natural conditions, it was reasonable to assume that health would be restored and maintained.*

Top Sergente leading the parade of champions at Dorchester Show, 1949, with Tony and Frank. (Photo: Herbert, Weymouth)

Cure your own Cattle was his accumulated experience of treating a range of cattle diseases in both his own herd and those of other breeders which he had taken in for treatment. Following success in restoring many of his own cattle to productive lives (including some he had also bought in, for between £5 and £15, as incurable) he advertised for other breeders' rejects on which to prove the validity of his methods. Frank's own prize winning senior stock bull Top Sergente, had a very strong pedigree and when he brought him into the herd he needed to establish his TB credentials: *His reaction to the tuberculin test was so violent that the Ministry would not allow retest and insisted on the disposal of the animal. But I could not afford to lose him and after moving him to some off land I gave him natural treatments and restored the deficiencies which gave rise to his toxaemia by careful diet of fresh food grown from virile soil. He was tested three times in the space of a year and showed a gradual improvement until at last, he was clear. The Ministry of Agriculture veterinary surgeon then gave him two clear tests at two monthly intervals and re-admitted him to the herd, free from disease, in which condition he has continued to do his work for the past five years showing no further sign of reaction.*

Top Sergente went on working for many more years, siring a large number of the Polden herd's most productive cows.

Foot and Mouth Disease

In 1951, there was an outbreak of foot and mouth disease in the UK mainland. In the six months from November 1951 to May 1952 four hundred herds were slaughtered, which

149

amounted to over one percent of the UK cattle population. Frank was convinced that animals fed on organically grown food would develop a natural immunity just as he had demonstrated in treating Johne's disease and other so called virally transmitted diseases. He was reinforced in this belief by the experience of Sir Albert Howard related in their discussions and as he had described in his book *Farming and Gardening for Health or Disease* (Faber,1940). During his time in India, Sir Albert secured six pairs of oxen for his small farm of 75 acres at Pusa to study their reaction to various infectious diseases when reared on composted, fertile pastures and free from the inoculations that were routinely given to large herds of cattle. He then brought his animals into contact with diseased cattle both by grazing on common pastures frequented by infected animals, and by allowing them to rub noses with FMD infected cattle over the hedges which bounded his farm and the large cattle sheds of the Pusa Estate. (Frank later did something similar when he smeared discharges from the udders of cattle infected with mastitis on healthy cow's udders without consequence.) Nothing happened to Sir Albert's cows and he was able to repeat his experiment in various other centres in India over a period of 26 years. *Foot and mouth disease is considered to be a viral disease. It could perhaps be more correctly described as a simple consequence of malnutrition either to the fact that the protein of the food has not been properly synthesised or to some obvious error in management. One of the most likely aggravations of the trouble is certain to be traced to the use of artificial manures instead of good old fashioned muck or compost.*

(Sir Albert Howard quoted in *Foot and Mouth Disease – a challenge*)

Frank decided to make an offer to the Ministry of Agriculture and the Chief Veterinary Officer which most cattle breeders would have regarded as positively bovicidal:

Goosegreen Farm
Sutton Mallet
Bridgwater
Chief Veterinary Officer
Animal Health Division
Ministry of Agriculture and Fisheries
Hook Rise, Tolwort, Surbition, Surrey 13th May 1952

Dear Sir

My experience with other cattle diseases leads me to ask if you would consider an experiment to investigate the possibilities of developing a natural immunity to foot-and-mouth disease. I have found in my own herd, ... that animals reared naturally from birth do not get Johne's disease and contagious abortion when brought in direct contact with infected animals, and it appears to be impossible mechanically to infect a healthy udder even by injecting the discharges from a virulent case of mastitis into the udder of the healthy animal.

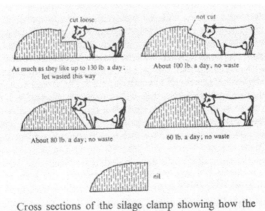

As much as they like up to 130 lb. a day; lot wasted this way

About 100 lb. a day, no waste

About 80 lb. a day; no waste

60 lb. a day; no waste

nil

Cross sections of the silage clamp showing how the quantity of silage a cow can take varies with the angle of the feeding face

Self-feeding silage. Diagram from Fertility Pastures, 1955

I believe that it might be possible to gain a similar immunity to foot and mouth disease for our cattle generally, and indeed, as we are told, foot and mouth infection is carried so easily and freely as on the feet of birds, natural immunity can be the only defence short of wiping out the whole bird population of Europe.

In an effort to test the possibilities of natural immunity I am prepared to make available animals of third generation of natural rearing and organic feeding, for placing together with similar animals reared and fed in the orthodox way, into an infected herd, or in direct contact with infection in some way to be decided by you...

Such experiments may not be possible in this country while the slaughter policy continues, but there could be no serious obstacle in the way of transferring animals to the

Continent, at least for the purposes of contact with infected animals.

I make this offer in the sincere hope that you will accept it as the constructive contribution of a practical farmer to a problem which has us all worried today more than ever before, and I shall be willing to meet you at your convenience to discuss details of ways and means of carrying my offer into effect.

Yours sincerely,
F NEWMAN TURNER

He also offered this as a preliminary trial to a more controlled comparison between calves reared conventionally and those reared and fed naturally, then allowing them, on reaching maturity, to mix freely with infected animals.

The Chief Veterinary Officer replied to say that as all experimental work on foot and mouth disease is done by the Foot and Mouth Disease Research Establishment at Purbright in Surrey, Frank should write to them. He did so with a copy of his proposal but, despite his reminders, he never received an acknowledgement or a reply.

Perhaps he was naïve in expecting a policy of slaughter – so firmly rooted in the belief that bacteria and viruses are the primary cause of disease from which no amount of natural immunity would offer protection – would be overturned.

Chapter 11

Putting Actions into Words

Rae Thompson was proficient in shorthand but Frank had to write in longhand for her to transcribe on an old Remington typewriter. (It was not until the early 1950s that he invested in a Grundig reel-to-reel tape recorder). With the demands of the farm and the Jersey herd, most of his writing had to be done at what would now be called 'unsocial hours' but that is a concept that did not exist in those days and certainly not in farming. Not that Rae was ever stinting in 'her devotion to the work of typing and re-typing the manuscript at all hours of the day and night, and for shouldering many tasks to relieve me for writing' as Frank acknowledged in his Preface to *Fertility Farming* when it was published in 1951.

There were often tight deadlines to be met with the need to publish *The Farmer* in a timely fashion for the growing list of subscribers, so it was surprising that he ever found the time for recreation and the demands of a growing family. But somehow, he did.

There were occasional evening cricket matches at neighbouring villages, usually played on a narrow mown strip in an otherwise tufty field. Frank would often bowl with his tongue between his teeth, a habit he had acquired at an early age when concentrating on any physical task (although probably not when he was boxing for Leeds University!). He did, however, describe how, on one occasion in the 1930s, driving in London, he had bitten through his tongue when he ran into the back of another vehicle. It didn't cure him of the habit.

Family holidays were always taken in Cornwall, staying with Lorna's parents, Matthew and Ella Clark, who had moved to Corbor, a semi-detached house on the A38 near St Erth, and a few miles south of Hayle, where her father managed a branch of Farm Industries. Corbor was within easy reach of some of the best beaches in Cornwall with St Ives, Carbis Bay, and Lelant accessible on the branch line from St Erth, and Penzance at the end of the main line. The summer was the busiest time on the farm with hay making and harvest so Lorna would take the train and us two boys to St Erth while Frank would drive down later for a few days when he could get away.

Soon there was a third son. On the 31st of July 1950, Adam Frank was born at Dr Pink's Stonefield maternity home in Blackheath. As the confinement approached Giles, then aged five, was parked with the Clarks at Corbor and, when the time came Frank, with me, drove Lorna up to Stonefield. After Adam's birth, Frank and I slept in the back of the Jowett Bradford station wagon parked overnight outside the nursing home.

When Frank was there with the station wagon, the family's favourite spot in Cornwall was Godrevy Point, near the lighthouse at the northern tip of St Ives Bay. Cars could be parked near a dry stone wall that gave some shelter for family picnics while the well-trodden turf of the path leading to the Point provided a reasonably smooth surface for cricket. Sometimes, on sunny Sundays, picnics at Godrevy would be shared with friends from Frank's university days, Brian and Jean Campbell, who farmed in the nearby village of Gwithian. We three boys and the three Campbell children, all learned to swim in one of the large rock pools on the beach below the green at Godrevy.

Lawrence D.Hills with his Bocking 14 strain of Russian Comfrey
(Photo: courtesy Garden Organic)

Fertility Farming had undergone a long gestation. As Frank wrote in his Preface: *Fertility Farming owes its existence to the inspiration of Sir Albert Howard, whose guidance and encouragement was the starting point of the work which it describes. When he urged me to write a book about my work at Goosegreen, he knew that my full time occupation as a working farmer would make its completion a matter of years; yet he went to considerable lengths to persuade me that it was a duty that must be fulfilled. I shall always regret that I was unable to complete the book before his death in 1947.*

As recorded earlier, as far back as 1946 Sir Albert had prompted Faber & Faber to publish Frank's book, so their Agricultural Editor, Richard de la Mare, was enthusiastic about the project by the late 1940s when he had had an opportunity to see the quality of Frank's writing in *The Farmer* and other publications. Faber's reader was Lawrence D Hills, a celebrated alpinist and horticultural writer, who made many valuable suggestions.

Fertility Farming was generally well received but inevitably ruffled the carefully standardised feathers of the agricultural correspondents and farming press: 'Successful farmer says "scrap the plough" '(Newcastle Journal, April 1951)'Fertility farmer has new disease theory' (Veld Trust, Johannesburg, July 1951)'He's scrapped his plough!' (Leicester Mail, 15th May 1951)'The author of this rather remarkable book claims that he brought to life a "dead farm" by getting its soil and its livestock "back to nature"' (New Commonwealth, June 1951)

But, not everyone was so receptive to Frank's assertions of nature's altruism. Sir George Stapleton, writing in The Sunday Times under the headline 'Militant Farmer,' had this to say: *Many who read this book will accept all that is said as inspired; others will regard the author as so biased that they will be sceptical of the validity of everything which he claims. My own attitude has been one of deep interest not undiluted with intense irritation. "Nature" by no means "destroys only the useless and unhealthy". That is typical of many statements which the facts of biology utterly disprove.*

(Sunday Times, 8th July 1951)

He goes on to say that because scientists are unwilling to make allowances for what science does not know *it is more important to refrain from dogmatising.*

The Veterinary Record was even more forthright: *This book is remarkable only for the aggressive naivety with which the author pursues his theme of "Fertility Farming" which is nothing more or less than the centuries old method of shallow surface culture combined with a heavy application of natural humus or compost – a method which man, with increasing populations to feed and the experience of the centuries behind him, has discarded in favour of greater efficiency ... On the whole, the aggressive presentation of the author's point of view will not commend this book to the majority of readers.*

(7th July 1951)

Meanwhile, Frank's second book, *Herdsmanship*, was well into production, so he was not to be deterred by the sceptical forces of orthodoxy. By now his radical approach was widely known: '*Mr Turner again.*

Mr Turner is an out and out believer in the magic of muck and is an oracle of organics ...

Whether or not Mr Turner will find any readers to agree with him, he puts his case vigorously and completely.'

(The Scotsman, 17th October 1952) *Farmer opposes slaughter policy of foot and mouth disease. "Bovine form of*

158

influenza '(Western Morning News 15th September 1952) *These muck and magic theories are unsound. But this new book on herdsmanship gives valuable hints.*

(Dairy Farmer, October1952) *He bases his theories for improving the health of dairy cattle on premises far from secure on a strictly scientific basis … Fundamentally of course, the author is pleading for a new approach in livestock husbandry. His plea for closer study of the animal's environment to promote positive health, rather to treat disease when it appears with neglect of the environment, is entirely commendable.*

(Cape Times, 6th December 1952)

Referring to the foot and mouth disease challenge, reprinted in *Herdsmanship*, David Stephen, the reviewer for The Scottish Field wrote: *The important thing isn't whether or not Turner is a crank, whether or not he is unscientific, or whether orthodox research is doing the best, or worst, it can. The important thing is that Turner has achieved certain results by certain methods, without the vast expenditure in time, money, and animal lives that we have come to accept as normal. His results ought to be investigated now, not in the spirit of an elder reproving an errant child, but to find out how he gets them. The business of calling names at Turner has gone far enough, and farther than we can afford. The pursuit of knowledge doesn't mean ignoring the line of inquiry you don't like, or arguing that the layman is an irritant. The fact is he doesn't irritate enough…When it comes to Foot and Mouth Disease, …he has declared that it need not occur if beasts are organically fed and properly managed…What he says in effect is: Take my beasts, place them in an infected herd. Let them rub noses with the affected beasts but let me feed my own during the trial (which is fair). And see what happens. Turner says his beasts will be resistant. Why isn't he taken on? It is criminal to avoid any possible answer to this scourge. It can't be, surely, that somebody is afraid of a man called Newman Turner.*

Well before publication of the books, there were plenty of people who were not afraid to visit Goosegreen to see for themselves how this new approach to agriculture, about which they had read in *The Farmer* and other periodicals or heard on the radio, was put into practice. They were writers, health reformers, some of them vegetarians and active in animal welfare. There were those with military backgrounds who had returned to their family farms after the war but also others of pacifist persuasions who had campaigned for peace before the war.

The husband and wife authors, Reginald Reynolds and Ethel Mannin, were two such people who were well-known for their left-wing views. They visited Goosegreen in September 1949. Reg Reynolds (1905-1958), a Quaker, had been general secretary of the No More War Movement in the mid-1930s and registered as a CO in the war, working in air raid precautions and mobile hospital units. After the war, he wrote critically of British imperialism in India and served as a mediator between Mahatma Gandhi and the British authorities. He wrote several books about Gandhi and the struggle for Indian independence. He and Mannin were married in 1938.

Ethel Mannin (1900-1984) was a prolific novelist and travel writer whose early communist sympathies were diluted following a visit to Stalinist Russia in 1936. She was also an avid football supporter but, given Frank's preference for rugby and cricket, conversations at Goosegreen were likely to have centred more on soil and socialism, than soccer.

Another writer, who was also a farmer and environmentalist, Elspeth Huxley (1907-97) visited Goosegreen in late 1949, while, in 1951, another Elspeth (Douglas Reid), an actress famous for her one woman shows, with which she toured the country during and after the war, was also a visitor. She was a vegetarian and an active campaigner for animal welfare – a theme which Frank brought to more prominence in later editions of *The Farmer* – and was later a co-founder of the Beauty Without Cruelty movement which sought to ban the use of animals in testing the safety of cosmetics.

A more exotic visitor to Goosegreen was the veterinary herbalist Juliette de Bairacli Levi, who was to play a prominent part in Frank and Lorna's lives over the next few years. Juliette had travelled widely in the Middle East and North Africa studying herbal lore in various countries, particularly among the Romany gypsies, with whom she lived for extended periods. She had written several books on the natural treatment of animals including the *Complete Herbal Handbook for Farm and Stable* published by Faber & Faber. She also wrote novels. Juliette had the appearance of a gypsy herself, with her dark skin and tousled black hair. Although born in England, her father was a Turkish businessman and her mother of Egyptian origin.

Elva Blacker painting Frank with Beeny at Goosegreen, 1951

When the cocker spaniel Roguey died in the late 1940s Frank and Lorna decided to get a boxer, Tessa, who became the farm dog. Early in 1949, she produced her first litter but developed mastitis so Frank and Lorna invited Juliette to visit and recommend herbal treatment for the bitch. The runt of Tessa's litter, and the only boy, was named by Giles, Beenboro. When he was born, Tessa was wandering across a small yard at the back of the farmhouse and he fell out on his head. It didn't do him any harm and he grew to be the biggest of the litter so Frank and Lorna kept him and his sister Julie, possibly named after Juliette. Beeny achieved his own immortality when he featured, with Frank, in a portrait painted by the artist Elva Blacker (1908-1984) in late 1951. Elva Blacker had painted portraits of many actors, writers, and health reformers including Dame Sybil Thorndike, George Bernard Shaw, and Dr Cyril Pink.

Juliette came to Goosegreen again after Christmas 1950, and, because she had been dissatisfied with the existing manufacturer of her formulae and their marketing strategy, Frank and Lorna had agreed to set up a company, Organic Herbal Products Ltd. which they based in premises at nearby Bridgwater. It was to manufacture and market Juliette's herbal veterinary products and other pet foods under the brand name of Herb Royal. It turns out that she was rather a difficult person to please as became evident from her correspondence with Frank in the ensuing years. After his experiences with the Tombreen venture, one might wonder at his resilience to face more tongue biting tensions but he managed to keep his sanity with the demands of the farm and *The Farmer*.

Then, there was also the cricket. He took up membership of Somerset County Cricket Club and, when the hay making and harvest permitted, took me to watch county games and the visiting Australian and South African teams at the county ground in Taunton. A bonus was that a gentleman farmer, called Ben Brocklehurst, who farmed in Berkshire for some years, was interested in Frank's farming methods, and played for Somerset, captaining the side in 1953 and 1954. In those days county teams were still captained by amateurs, although Brocklehurst was one of the last to do so. He wasn't particularly successful as Somerset lost 37 of the 56 games played under his leadership and remained bottom of the

County Championship but at least he could take my autograph book into the dressing rooms and secure the signatures of some of the most famous English cricketers of the early 1950s such as Len Hutton, Jonny Wardle, and the Bedser twins.

Rae Thompson
(1914-1998)

Rachel Thompson was a young lady from the North of England who was to become a pivotal part of Frank's work for many years. She was working at Friend's House, the headquarters of the Society of Friends (Quakers), on Euston Road in London when, in 1948, her friend, Grace Clark, who was one of the founder members of the Whole Food Society, suggested she should go along to a meeting of the Society that was being held there.

Rae had become a vegetarian and had long been interested in the food reform movement. After the meeting, Frank invited her to meet him for an interview the following day at the London Dairy Show where *The Farmer* had a stand. Shortly afterwards, Rae joined the small team at Goosegreen Farm where her typing and secretarial skills were put to good use in assisting with the publications and organisation of the weekend courses.

In *Fertility Farming*, Frank acknowledged her *devotion to the work of typing and retyping the manuscript at all hours of day and night, and for shouldering many other tasks to relieve me for writing*. Rae typed all Frank's manuscripts and the many thousands of other words he authored and she remained his, and the family's secretary, for over twenty years, living in the modest accommodation that was available at each of the houses to which we moved. She was also a keen gardener and spent much of her spare time in the gardens at Goosegreen, Ferne, and Deanrow.

Chapter 12

Herb Royal

Stresses and successes

The Spring 1950 edition of *The Farmer* carried the first advertisement for Herb Royal veterinary herbs with the strap line, 'the only herbal products mentioned in Juliette de Bairacli Levy's latest and most important book The Cure of Canine Distemper and Hard Pad'. Following their meetings at Goosegreen in 1949 and 1950, Frank and Juliette had decided to pool their expertise in natural animal treatments. Juliette had become dissatisfied with the existing manufacturer of her herbal formulae. She was the author of several books on the treatment and rearing of dogs, being herself, a breeder of Afghan Hounds. She had travelled extensively in Europe and the Middle East, living with gypsies and farmers, and acquired an extensive knowledge of herbal lore. After Organic Herbal Products was incorporated, Juliette assigned to Frank the exclusive rights to her formulae which he was to manufacture under the brand name Herb Royal. *The Farmer* announcement carried the following endorsement from Juliette: *My herbal products have come to a permanent home at Cornhill, Bridgewater within easy reach of the technical advice and veterinary experience of Mr Newman Turner NDA, NDD, editor of The Farmer who has worked alongside me in my herbal work. Thus, I can guarantee that my carefully tested formulae and dosage will never be adulterated and the highest standard of my products will always be maintained.*

Child labour. The author (aged 10) was put to work spreading droppings on the ley, 1950. (Photo: Douglas Allen)

Among the first products they supplied were Garlic tablets (with foenugreek) as a treatment for infectious ailments;

Seaweed Blend, as a source of minerals and iodine and as a tonic for the coats and for whelping bitches; and Tree Barks Blend, as a nutritious food for brood bitches, puppies, and calves. Many of these were based on herbs that Frank had often used in treatment of his cattle. Cases of mastitis, for example, were fasted and dosed with an infusion of garlic, and received enemas as part of a cleansing regimen. Later, other innovative products were added to the Herb Royal range, such as Seabics, a dog food based on seaweed, Chewsticks (an idea that doesn't seem to have been patented and was, therefore, soon imitated by large scale pet food manufacturers), and their most successful product, Budgerigar Seed Rings. These consisted of sesame seed in a vegetable paste mounted on cardboard rings that could be threaded on a perch in the birdcage.

Before these products were created, Frank had to recruit a manager for the company and a local agricultural engineer was engaged, initially on a part time basis in 1952, and later by 1953, as managing director. Hans Lederman lived in the village of Spaxton, near Bridgewater, and had the skills to negotiate with suppliers of the raw materials and machinery, to manufacture the products.

The business relationship with Juliette did not get off to a good start. She may not have been aware of the realities in time and effort, of setting up a company and launching its products. As the author of several books, she was also prolific in her letter writing on such matters as publicity of the products and customer service. On two closely typed pages of foolscap dated 6th March 1950, she wrote to Frank to complain that he had had the business for nearly three months, yet she had seen no proper advertising and deliveries were slow according to the reports she had received from her clients. She also wrote that Motherwort, used in Birth Aid Blend to assist whelping, *should not be used in any more herbal blends bearing my name. To put a finely barbed herb into most medicine is wrong, even in brewing there is a danger from the barbs. Wild marjoram must be used instead to make the third herb of the Birth Aid Blend.* Frank responded by stating that *obviously the only person capable of running the business to your satisfaction is yourself. If you were at least consistent one could tolerate your periodic insults or should I say one of my patience could, for I am sure no one else would* and went on to describe how he and Lorna had spent long hours packing and chasing printers who were reluctant to undertake the work of producing leaflets at the time of the General Election (in February 1950). He also explained that supplies were, as far as possible, sent out immediately on receipt of the orders. Frank also pointed out that the inclusion of Motherwort had been verbally agreed before in a telephone conversation and that, unless she could get some clarity of thought, they should go their separate ways for business in order to preserve their friendship. To which Juliette responded *I have a thousand and one character faults myself, I know all too well. I think your main fault is carelessness and too hurried action.*

Successes

These thunderous rumblings did something to clear the clouds that hung over the venture, for Juliette subsequently suggested they draw up the agreement for the assignment of all rights to her veterinary formulae to Frank in return for a royalty of five percent on their sales. She also suggested that her books, including a novel, *Look, the Wild Swans*, could be sold through The Farmer Publications and that she might write an occasional article for *The Farmer*. Frank had also interceded with Richard de la Mare at Faber and Faber to reconsider Juliette's new novel, *The Bride of Lew*, which they had rejected as being too long. He suggested that she comply with their request to shorten the novel somewhat and it was eventually accepted by them.

Juliette continued to make requests for supplies and payment of the Herb Royal earnings, *as I absolutely want to have the money to help me to get to Palestine and I have to pay my passage* and then, in conclusion *Give Lorna and the children my sincere love. Giles was so adorable at the station his thin little voice calling back "goodbye Juliette". I did get all my pieces of baggage to Harrogate safely*. An assignment of the rights was agreed, the business grew and relations appeared to remain cordial punctuated by lengthy correspondence and requests from Juliette for payment of her royalties as well as the remainder of the sum of £500 they had agreed for the purchase of the rights. *If you had really wanted my business you could well have sold a cow or two before now*, she wrote.

OHP set up an Animal Health Association through which subscribers could seek advice from both Juliette and Frank on livestock related concerns. They also took a stand at Crufts, the national dog show held annually at the Olympia exhibition centre in London, and Juliette wrote afterwards to say how much she had enjoyed working there with Hans and Rae Thompson.

****

In the mid-1950s the BBC broadcast a popular series of TV programmes about pets called Smokey Club, presented by the zoologist, George Cansdale. Frank appeared on several editions of these, giving advice on natural feeding of dogs. He prepared a puppy feeding chart, which viewers were invited to send for. Unfortunately, it bore the name of Herb Royal and mentioned some of their products. This was in breach of the BBC's strict prohibition of any commercial bias at that time, and, when the producer saw them, Frank was quickly dropped from the programme.

****

Stresses

Hans Lederman ran OHP with a teutonic efficiency. He kept a keen eye on the financial health of the company which, like any offspring lacking a strong genetic endowment, being short of capital, was frail and prone to periodic crises. But, for Frank, who from 1953, was juggling the transition from Goosegreen to Ferne Farm and keeping *The Farmer's* publication on schedule, it was essential for OHP to be in good hands, as particularly since the move to Wiltshire he was no longer close at hand for the day to day running of the business. Hans was soon irritated by the demands from various corners of Europe made by Juliette. On one occasion, she had suggested that, part of her royalties should be sent direct to several people who had lent her money. *Regarding the bitch in Portugal*, Hans wrote in 1953, *I have really thought a lot about her and I have come to the definite conclusion that there is no reason whatsoever why we should pay her royalties for anything else but her formulae.*

170

Whether or not, the three way stretch in the affairs of the company was a hindrance to its ultimate success, it was certainly a three way stress for Frank and Lorna. Relations between Juliette and OHP slowly soured and with them her friendship with the family. What part Hans Lederman's impatience with her carping, and Frank's preoccupation with his other enterprises had to play in this is difficult to fathom. Alleging that OHP was altering her formulae, Juliette sought to disassociate herself from the company and to terminate the agreement. But she had gone elsewhere with her formulae and attempted to remove their name from her books, whereupon OHP sued her for breach of contract. In a lengthy affidavit, running to fourteen pages of foolscap, she cited her many successes in treating animals and accused Frank and Hans of misrepresenting her by continuing to use her name on OHP products and leaflets. In the way that legal matters can drag on – and as they would turn out to in respect of disputes that were to come at Ferne – claims and counter claims flew back and forth but they never went to court. OHP paid Juliette what she was entitled to under the terms of the agreement and withdrew the litigation.

As the dissent with Juliette began to fade, other worries were surfacing in the form of Hans Lederman's requests for greater say in the company's management. He argued, quite legitimately, that turnover had increased under his management and was able to produce figures to support this growth over the years he had been running the company. In the mid-1950s, he expressed concern about the amount that Frank was taking out of the business by way of advisory fees, director's fee, and even a contribution to the publishing of *The Farmer*. He set out his own contributions in terms of finance, including a guarantee of the bank overdraft by mortgaging his life insurance.*27ᵗʰ February 1956*

My only wish is to be helpful, but if you persist in these drawings it will land us in the bankruptcy court in spite of increasing sales.

Frank reiterated his assurance, that he had always regarded Hans as a partner in the business, but emphasised his position in clear terms:*22ⁿᵈ March 1956*

I must make my position quite clear and take the consequences and I do it in writing as it is evident that I did not make myself clear when we last met.

May I reiterate what I said then that I had always considered you to be in the position of a partner and always treated you as such except that as it was my business (or more strictly my wife's) that we were building, I would not expect for the present to take the same income from it as you. The reasons for me not taking anything like the same proportionate income in ratio even to my contribution in actual day to day work, has been obvious throughout. The whole of my work is directed towards the building of that business for the future rather than the present. I have taken nothing from my books or The Farmer as I have considered them essential pillars in the building of Organic Herbal Products. Even the farm has latterly had to help them because I felt that I must keep The Farmer and the writing going as an essential part of the Organic Herbal Products' future. So, in effect, my whole time, day and much of the night, has been and is for Organic Herbal Products. For all that, I am trying to limit my takings to £10 or so a week and even that is not a personal drawing, but again largely used to further the information and knowledge which is the lifeblood of Organic Herbal Products. I am conscious all the time, that my farming is the experimental basis of Organic Herbal Products. There is no great living in it, but I feel, like The Farmer and my books, they must be kept going for the sake of Organic Herbal Products and the better living which should come in this way (i.e. via OHP) one day.

Though, at 43 I am often reminded that, for the hours of work I put in, my family should be enjoying better results. I have felt that my slaving might be a substitute for the capital, which I could get someone else to put into Organic Herbal Products, but with the difference that, though my family and I might have to wait longer for the financial rewards, at least we can avoid relinquishing control of the business and our future.

Compromises were made, Frank retained control, and Hans made periodic threats of resignation but they both had too much at stake to allow things to crumble. Lorna's father, Matthew Clark, was persuaded to become a director and injected a small amount of capital in return for shares as did Lorna, who was already a director.

Frank with George Cansdale (L) and Hans Lederman at opening of
Animal Fare in Bridgwater. (Photo: Douglas Allen)

The business grew with sales to Germany and the USA among others and setbacks, such as an episode in which the supply of Tree Barks Blend had resulted in the deaths of several dogs, to which it had been fed. It turned out the batch of the slippery elm bark powder, which was the main ingredient, was contaminated with traces of strychnine. The suppliers of the powder to Herb Royal admitted liability and paid the compensation to the pet owners, but it damaged OHP's reputation. Sales of Budgerigar Seed Rings suffered when Japanese manufacturers copied them and undercut Herb Royal, particularly in the American market.

The company moved to a factory, newly built on the outskirts of Bridgewater by the local council, and a shop,

Animal Fare, was opened in the town by George Cansdale. This supplied OHP products and other pet accessories.

The vicissitudes of the cut throat commercial world are normal for any business and perhaps, also, there is often a magma of discontent simmering beneath the executive surface. Every so often the larva breaks through the surface but the volcanic eruptions were yet to come.

Chapter 13

Ferne Farm

A tale of poached pastures, litigation, and
rampant goats

The Ferne Estate, on the borders of Wiltshire and Dorset, near
the abbey town of Shaftesbury, was the country seat of the
thirteenth Duke of Hamilton who had purchased it in 1914.
After his death in 1940 his son, Douglas-Hamilton (against
whom Frank had, rather improbably, claimed to have boxed
when at Leeds University) succeeded to the title. His mother,
Nina, Dowager Duchess of Hamilton continued to live at
Ferne.

During the Second World War, she had set up an animal
sanctuary for the pets of bomb victims and service personnel
to keep them out of harm's way. Inevitably, a number of these
animals were not reclaimed after the war and the Ferne
Animal Sanctuary was established on a more permanent basis.

In her will, drawn up in 1944, the Duchess appointed her
son, the fourteenth Duke, and her friend Miss L. Lind af
Hageby, as executors and stipulated that her home and estate
be used as an institute 'for the treatment by non-vivisectional
means of caring for children and animals … or methods of

healing disassociated from experiments on animals, such as nature cure, homoeopathy, herbalism, manipulative treatment, osteopathy … vegetarian and fruitarian systems of dietetics and psychotherapeutics.' In 1906, with her friend, Lind af Hageby, the Duchess had founded the Animal Defence and Anti-Vivisection Society which did much for animal welfare in the inter war years.

****

Miss Lizzie Lind af Hageby (1878-1963)

Lizzy Lind af Hageby was born in Sweden and moved to England in 1902, to study at the London School of Medicine for Women. She became a prominent anti-vivisectionist and feminist campaigner and co-founded The Animal Defence and Anti-Vivisection Society with the Duchess of Hamilton in 1906.

She was an eloquent speaker, and conducted her own case when suing The Pall Mall Gazette for libel, after it had accused her of 'a systematic campaign of falsehood'. Although she lost the case, the judge praised her eloquence and skill in cross examination.

Lind af Hageby was also involved in several women's organisations, linked to peace initiatives and the suffragette movement believing that if women could vote there would be greater attention to animal welfare.

****

Following the death of the Duchess in January 1951, the management of the estate and sanctuary became the responsibility of Miss Lind. The estate, however, was saddled with heavy death duties and the executors were faced with having to sell it, which threatened the future of the sanctuary. But they were able to raise the funds, with the help of the ADAVS, and ownership of the home farm came under the control of Miss Lind. Her sanctuary superintendent was a Miss Mollie Atherton, assisted by a kennel maid.

Later in 1951, Miss Lind wrote to Frank proposing that, he should become her adviser on farming matters. This was followed by a letter in January 1952 offering him the post of Personal Advisor at a salary of £500 for one year, which Frank accepted. A company, Ferne Farm Ltd, was set up and incorporated in 1952 with the object of pursuing the objectives the Duchess had set out in her will. The shareholders were listed as Eric T Ivory, honorary secretary of the Scottish Society for the Prevention of Vivisection, Dr M Beddow Bayley, a medical practitioner and prominent anti-vivisection campaigner, F Eveleen Seton, Chairman of the National Gardens Guild, and Frank.

This seemed to be a unique opportunity for him to rejuvenate another larger farm, while helping to establish an animal hospital, in conjunction with the sanctuary, and run on natural treatment principles. Frank and Lorna set about seeking a purchaser for Goosegreen Farm and, eventually, it was sold to F C Carr, a well-known West Country herbalist and landowner who ran a small spa at Shipham, a village in the heart of the Mendip Hills in north Somerset. Frank, Lorna, and the family, together with Rae Thompson and the pedigree Jersey herd, moved to Ferne Farm in April 1953.

****

****

Ferne House was a three storey mansion with a two storey servants' wing built in 1830, on the site of the first house, which dated back to the sixteenth century. The colonnaded front aspect looked across a lawn, the old tennis court, and fields towards a chalk escarpment, the pinnacle of which was Wyn Green, the highest point in Wiltshire. Eight rooms on the top floor, provided accommodation for the family and Rae as well as a couple of rooms for an office, and storage space for the publications. A further room, on the ground floor by the side entrance, was used as a subscription office for *The Farmer*.

The whole estate comprised 500 acres, although the home farm was about half of that. Three farm cottages provided accommodation for farm workers, and, nearby, were stables, barns, and a milking parlour adjoined by a dairy, a Victorian structure, built on a raised stone platform with arches beneath to improve ventilation. The stable yard was entered by a fine stone archway, and many of the sanctuary cats and dogs were housed in pens there. Grazing in the parkland behind the house, were a number of horses, some of which were in retirement from the war years, or had been rescued from mines. One had even been a waltzing circus pony. (When I later had an opportunity to ride it, it tended to walk sideways as if performing).

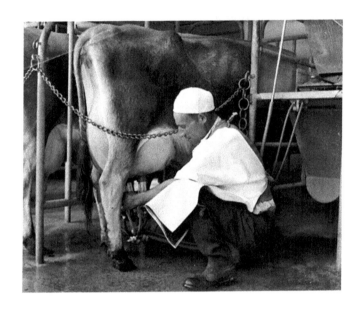

Tony Capozzoli in the milking parlour at Goosegreen.
(Photo: Douglas Allen)

Ferne seemed to be an ideal combination – a centre where care and compassion for animal welfare would be combined with an agricultural experiment that placed humanitarian principles and co-operation with nature at its heart. The unpredictable element was the capriciousness of human nature.

The family settled into a life in an environment, somewhat different from that of the Somerset levels. Ferne is about 500 feet above sea level. The undulating parkland is bounded by woods, which had harboured foxes, deer and abundant rabbits. The hollow, near the main drive, which sheltered the old ice house, an essential feature of country houses before the invention of refrigerators, was now overgrown, and provided an ideal environment for an extensive badger sett, where Giles and I could go on nocturnal badger watching expeditions. (Badgers favour a chalky landscape about 500 feet above sea level) The family were also able to join in the celebrations on a rainy day in June 1953 at the nearby village of Donhead St Andrew, to celebrate the coronation of Queen Elizabeth II. All the local children were given souvenir coronation mugs.

Frank set about building the fertility of the soil at the Ferne home farm where much of the arable land and pastures had been poorly managed. It was necessary to establish herbal leys with deep rooting plants to reach the mineral rich layers of the underlying chalk. Many of the fields that had been neglected were foul, that is they were heavily infested with weeds, such as docks and charlock, which it was necessary to manage with a careful programme of mowing, ploughing then re-seeding and laying fallow, that subsequently became a contentious issue with Miss Lind and her advisors.

To assist fertility, the hen houses, for the flock of Rhode Island Reds, were moved across the meadows as the hens roamed free range. For their own safety, they had to be shut in at night after they went in to roost. But the early 1950s saw the arrival of myxomatosis, an unpleasant viral disease, which decimated the rabbit population, so starving foxes became much bolder, and often conducted their marauding trips in broad daylight. Invariably they would slaughter several hens before taking one back to their lair for the cubs (unlike badgers who prefer earthworms, mice and voles and never take food back to the sett).

The Farmer continued to be 'published and edited from the farm', but it was now Ferne Farm and, as subscriptions and advertising revenue increased to serve the demand for organic farming and gardening products, Stanley Bentley was installed in the ground floor offices, as Subscription and Accounts Manager. The Bentleys were a family of Jehovah's Witnesses, and lived in one of the farm cottages near the stable yard. Frank also had the Herb Royal business to oversee at a distance, with occasional trips back to Bridgewater, where the business was growing under the management of Hans Lederman.

Then there was the third book in Frank's organic trilogy to be completed for Faber & Faber. This meant more evening, weekend, and holiday writing: *As I write, I sit in a field of perhaps forty or fifty acres which is at present hardly capable of feeding the rabbits who share it with a few hungry store bullocks. The field adjoins a quiet seashore on one of the loveliest corners of the Cornish coast. Every year for the past ten years I have come here to write, while my sons play on the sands below; or to play cricket on this unproductive turf in the energetic interludes between writing, when I fancy myself emulating my fellow Yorkshireman, Freddie Trueman. Here are forty or fifty wasted acres, upon which, on occasions, I cannot even enjoy expending my cricketing energy, because of the swarms of seaweed flies which breed in the piles of seaweed accumulating on the sands a few yards below. And yet all this land needs, to make it grow a first class pasture, to enable it to carry a cow to the acre, is about a tenth of the seaweed that is deposited alongside each Autumn. It would not even be necessary to mix with it the sewage sludge that pours out into the surrounding sea from two adjoining towns; though, if such an obvious invitation of nature were ever to be accepted by the local authorities, there is no reason why this now useless land could not carry two cows to the acre for the greater part of the year.*

(Fertility Pastures,1955)

Fertility Pastures was published in 1955. In the passage quoted above, Frank was emphasising the importance of the Rule of Return, and the need for animal manure to retain a healthy soil structure. The springy turf of the green, at Godrevy Point, was ideal for holiday cricket, but, in common with many moorland areas, he believed, could provide more productive pastures with better (organic) land management.

Fertility Pastures had the usual mixed reception, and Jorian Jenks, writing in *Mother Earth* (which he edited for the Soil Association) observed that 'Some of the chapters are wrongly numbered and there is evidence of over hasty proof reading'. Perhaps not surprising, given the somewhat windswept conditions under which Frank laboured (although some responsibility must be placed at the door of Richard de la Mare's editorial department at Faber & Faber). Jenks went on to say: *'The most interesting chapter is the one in which the author described when he "consulted the cow" by laying down small plots of the 35 species and strains housed in his herbal lays and gave his cattle access to these'.*

The Field, a magazine directed at large scale landowners wrote; *Not everyone will agree with the author's deductions from his own and published observations but the book is unquestionably a thought provoking one.*

(The Field 19th April 1955)

The spirit of collaboration at Ferne, did not last long and relations between farm and sanctuary gradually became more toxic. Whether or not, the blame for 'people poisoning' could be laid at the feet of Mollie Atherton, the Sanctuary Superintendent, or David Coulsey and Frances Dykes, the late Duchess's butler and housekeeper, who lived quietly in the servants' wing, Miss Lind started to object to the occupation of the office space on the ground floor, the publication business being run from Ferne, and the way in which Frank was running the farm. Although having agreed verbally to the use of the office space and management of the land on organic principles, she engaged a firm of agricultural advisers, Wooley and Wallis, to submit a report to her that showed little understanding of the difficulties of bringing neglected arable land back to fertility. In April 1956, not long before the tenth birthday celebrations of *The Farmer*, Frank received a letter from solicitors acting for Miss Lind alleging mismanagement of the land, occupation of office space without consent, and neglect and cruelty to livestock, and giving notice to terminate all existing arrangements between them, and vacate the house and farm 'with all his chattels, animals, employees, and effects' by the 30th September 1956.

They did not comply with this, claiming tenancy under the Agricultural Holdings Act, effectively sitting tenants. As had been the case with Tombreen nearly ten years before, the question of whether Frank had been a tenant or a manager became a bone of contention. After they failed to move out of Ferne, Miss Lind issued a writ in November 1956 alleging:

- neglect and damage to the farm buildings;
- unhygienic management of livestock by permitting them to live in unsanitary conditions;
- cruelty to a tethered bull (alleged by Miss Atherton to have been left out overnight in a heavy rainstorm);
- mismanagement of pastures and failure to cultivate (based on the observations of the firm of agricultural surveyors);
- extending without consent agreed occupation of the house for publishing offices of The Farmer;

and claiming damages for trespass and payment of profits of the farming activities.

Legal claims and counter claims then followed, and, in further elaboration of the 'misdemeanours', Miss Lind alleged: 'He has failed to manage the said farm in accordance with the principles of humane farm management, animal welfare and hygiene, and preservation of the soil which the Plaintiff and Defendant had agreed ... should be put into practical operation at the said farm. Instead the Defendant has neglected the soil ... he has neglected the welfare and hygiene of the farm animals by permitting them to live under insanitary and filthy conditions with great accumulations of dung and dirt in the cow court and dirt and disorder in the stabling with resultant smells; and he has ill-treated farm animals by such cruel practices as the treatment of sterile cows by fasting and the tethering of a bull in a field at night during a heavy rain storm'.

It was clear that Miss Lind, or perhaps more specifically, Miss Atherton, had not read Frank's books and articles or grasped any idea of the rationale behind the humanitarian and organic principles which he applied. He was able to make a robust rebuttal of these allegations, and prepared a detailed report of the state of the farm buildings, and the state of the farmland prior to his arrival at Ferne, supported by the report of an independent inspection by Friend Sykes, an experienced organic farmer who lived on the Wiltshire downs not far from Ferne. Sykes had found that, a number of fields had been heavily poached by the trampling of livestock in winter, and others had long-term infestation of thistles and docks. The foreman at Ferne, Mr Allen, had informed Frank that some years previously an attempt had been made by the farm manager, with a gang of men, to have the docks pulled out and carted off but, following a dispute with the Duchess, the docks were spread and ploughed in! Frank had explained to Wooley and Wallis that he had divided one field into several sections as a dock control experiment, using a number of different methods of cultivation alongside the different methods of control and weed killing sprays, but they appeared to have ignored this in their report. Well timed mowing of meadows and parkland would normally improve the leys by providing a mulch, and this had changed some of the pastures for the better since Frank had taken up tenancy but with the ongoing dispute he had curtailed cultivation. Of the park land Friend Sykes had written:... *the land should have received thorough summer tillage to clean it. Then the ley should have been sown and then after that the fields should have been managed with skill and understanding of good farming practice. Instead of this, horses had been allowed to plunge about doing no end of damage and the field, whilst not absolutely useless in its present condition, is almost so*

through the carelessness with which the animals have been
allowed to poach and destroy the newly established grasses.

Sykes had also commented on the poor state of the grassland in other parts of the parkland, and that there were too many trees, a number of which had fallen making cultivation difficult. Several attempts to crop the polo field at the eastern boundary of the farm, were frustrated by the persistent grazing of the herd of sanctuary goats from the adjoining paddock. 'A crop of seed oats was sown from new expensive seed the year before last and virtually ruined by the grazing over the whole field by these goats and last year the field was fallowed. Following the fencing of a portion of the field through which the goats were given access by Miss Atherton, a further attempt had been made to grow a crop in this field but a section of the fence has been opened and made into a small gateway from the goat paddock, presumably by Miss Atherton's staff, and the goats have been turned into the field deliberately practically every day, and they have grazed the growing crop of oats, peas, and vetches, continuously since the time it started growing. It was noticed that the goats were not turned on to the field on the day that the inspection was made by Messrs Wooley and Wallis.'

As to animal cruelty, Frank only had to remind them of the hardiness of Jersey cattle in winter conditions, and, regarding the unhygienic conditions alleged by Miss Atherton: *The manure, is allowed to accumulate in the yards throughout the winter, and similarly in any loose boxes in which calves and calving cows are housed. So, as long as, clean straw is spread each day, so that the animal has a perfectly clean bed on which to lie the dung below, adds comfort and warmth to the animal. The hard labour of daily 'mucking out' is avoided, and the only portion of the cattle sheds, which has to be cleaned, is the milking parlour, which is no more than the width of eight cows. As the cows pass through quickly we generally manage each milking time without any dung being made in the parlour itself. A swill down with cold water hose after milking quickly cleans and freshens the floor of the milking parlour in readiness for the next milking.*

When the spring sowing is done, and the cows and young stock are all out at grass – in other words when there is little other productive work to be done – we make a large scale attack   on the manure in the yards and sheds. This is carted out with tractor, trailer and horse cart to close up the site of the compost heaps and compost is made as we clean out the yards.

(Fertility Farming, p106)

The litigious letters, continued to fly to and fro while the uncertainty of their future at Ferne, hindered any long term planning with the farm. Were they to capitulate or challenge the threat of eviction and claim for breach of contract? The latter course of action would inevitably lead to the High Court and crippling legal costs. The Ferne fiasco was eventually overtaken by new directions in Frank's life with the publications, and a diversification from animal to human health.

His successful restoration to their working herds of a number of breeders' cows, by nature cure and herbal treatments prompted them to ask Frank, if he could suggest anything to help some problems they had with their own health. He had acquired a wide knowledge of medicinal herbs, and spent some time with the leading medical herbalists, particularly those in the north of England, who had large practices. In 1956, he successfully sat the final examinations of the Faculty of Herbal Medicine, and was admitted to membership of the National Institute of Medical Herbalists. An opportunity to become a consultant for the Society of Herbalists, which ran the Culpeper shops, founded by Mrs C F Lyle, helped Frank to make the momentous decision to give up farming, sell the pedigree Jersey herd, and move to Letchworth Garden City in north Hertfordshire.

Deanrow in Letchworth Garden City, 1958

The pressure to leave the fractious environment of Ferne was eased by the generosity of an osteopath friend, Robert Scrutton, who ran a small residential nature cure clinic at Middle Woodford, a village just outside the cathedral city of Salisbury in Wiltshire. They moved the publications office into temporary accommodation at the appropriately named

Heale House in the summer of 1958, while they sought a suitable property in Letchworth.

Grace Clarke had been a regular attender of the weekend courses at Goosegreen Farm, and it was she who had persuaded Rae Thomson to apply for the post of secretary, to Frank in 1948. She also became a debenture holder in F. Newman Turner Ltd, so Frank wrote to inform her of the change of plans:

2nd July 1958

I think Rae has told you of our proposed move. We have at last accepted a settlement which involves our leaving rather than going through further months of waiting and then paying for High Court Action to retain possession. We have got compensation though not enough to buy another farm. So, I have decided to concentrate on my human healing work which seems to have a much greater immediate value and directly helps many more people than running one farm. By working on the consumer end, one can persuade many more people to demand properly grown food and hasten the day when more farmers will have to provided it in a way that I could never do by growing for a very few people and trying (mostly in vain) to persuade other farmers to do the same.

...FNT Ltd will continue in existence and acquire the publishing company I formed, thus enabling me to use some tax losses to offset any publishing and consulting profits. But I hope, after the sale of the major part of the herd and implements, to pay off your debenture.

They would leave behind the fractious environment of Ferne, but the turbulence of the fifties pursued them in the form of Herb Royal and the ever present financial insecurities of publishing.

Chapter 14
Global Threats and Fiscal Struggles

Campaigning and publishing on a shoestring

The devastation inflicted by the atom bombing of the Japanese cities of Hiroshima and Nagasaki in 1945, must have shocked pacifists such as Frank, Reginald Reynolds, and Hugh Schonfield, and many others who would not accept that even the ending of World War Two could justify the massive loss of innocent lives. The long term consequences were yet to become apparent, but it strengthened their resolve to do all they could, to make sure it would not happen again. All three were writers who, through their various publications, could perhaps make a small contribution to greater awareness of the potential global threats of nuclear fallout.

Lorna, with Reginald Reynolds, Ethel Mannin, and boxer pups,
Goosegreen, 1949

Frank's medium was *The Farmer*, and when atmospheric
nuclear testing began in the early 1950s, there were serious
concerns about the effects of radioactive fallout on plant,
animal, and human health. When Lawrence D Hills began to
receive, with greater frequency, than had been normal, reports
and photographs of plant mutations, he wrote an article for
The Farmer and suggested the likelihood of these being

related to nuclear fallout. Frank decided to run Lawrence's article in the summer 1957 edition of *The Farmer* under the headline 'Must Man Mutate to Monster?' As Frank wrote in his editorial, Leaning on the Gate, Good ends can never justify bad means.

Lawrence was intrigued by the letters and photographs in *The Field* magazine, suggesting that there were more freak plants than usual in 1956. He wrote an article for *The Guild Gardener*, another horticultural magazine, inviting more evidence. He was able to ascertain that, there were significantly more freak Lupins in 1957, particularly among the crops of commercial growers, but also of Foxgloves, and some other species. He discounted the possibility, that these were the result of viral infection, weedkillers, pesticides, or fertilisers, and surmised that genetic distortions were the consequence of plants taking up Caesium 137, a radioactive compound released into the atmosphere by nuclear fission, and absorbing this in place of potassium, when they were short of that mineral. The million plus circulation magazine *Illustrated* had commissioned an article by Lawrence but cut it severely by publication, and it attracted fewer letters than the front page splash in *The Farmer*, with its modest circulation of a few thousand. In his autobiography *Fighting Like the Flowers* (1989) Lawrence D Hills wrote: *Newman Turner was an editor of an earlier tradition…He gave me the space I wanted to say what I wanted to say about the news I had gathered. I was trying to warn the world that nuclear tests could have set nature's alarm bells ringing and I hoped to find plants or varieties of plants that would be super sensitive to radioactive isotopes concentrated from fallout.*

Lawrence appealed for more research to pursue this line of enquiry, and Frank, even had a slip placed in that edition of *The Farmer*, suggesting readers buy an extra copy to send to their MP.

This was an example of Frank's various campaigns and concerns achieving some sort of coalescence. Perhaps, the peace initiatives of his earlier life had been overtaken by the environmental and organic on which he felt compelled to act, but nuclear proliferation was a potential threat to peace and had strong environmental and health implications. Governments seemed set on the power of weaponry, and what became known as the 'nuclear deterrent' just as in the immediate post war years, they were determined to promote the use of chemicals on the land, to increase productivity regardless of the long term consequences. (The implications of the latter were strikingly brought to widespread public awareness by the publication of Rachel Carson's book *Silent Spring* in 1962.) The foundation of the Campaign for Nuclear Disarmament in 1957 by Bruce Kent, supported by Bertrand Russell and Canon John Collins, provided a platform for widespread public protest. For several years they organised protest marches at Easter from Aldermaston, the Atomic Weapons Research Establishment, to London's Trafalgar Square but it was The Committee of 100, a breakaway group from the CND led by Russell, that advocated a campaign of civil disobedience.

On the 11th September 1961, Frank and Lorna, accompanied by my brothers and me, joined an estimated twelve to fifteen thousand protesters at Trafalgar Square for a sit down demonstration in defiance of a government ban on any assembly in central London. It was to be followed by a march to Parliament Square. Demonstrators were instructed to disobey any requests by police to move on and to remain inert, so the family sat in the road on the north side of the square near the National Gallery. Over a thousand arrests were made that day. It took three burly policemen to carry Frank to a nearby police van. The following week the local paper carried the following story: *'Local people arrested in demonstration'*.

A school teacher, an osteopath, a housewife, schoolboy and student were among more than a dozen local people arrested during the "Ban the Bomb" demonstration in Trafalgar Square on. Sunday ...

'At Old Street Court on Tuesday 48 years old osteopath Frank Newman Turner and his wife Lorna, of Deanrow, Pasture Road, Letchworth were each fined £2 for their part in the demonstration. 'They admitted disregarding police directions for preventing obstruction and were said to have been sitting side by side on the road in Trafalgar Square. They appeared before the Court separately and Mrs Newman Turner told the magistrate, Mr Harold Sturge: "These are the only means whereby one can express what I consider to be the moral conscience of a large section of the people of this country" 'After hearing a policeman say that she sat in the road and refused to move Mrs Newman Turner said "I didn't refuse to move. I did move voluntarily. I asked to be arrested" 'Mr Sturge: "Did you remain sitting after you knew it was the direction of the Commissioner that you should not?"

"Oh yes," she added, "I regret the inconvenience to the police, but I undertook it in the same spirit that I undertake to protect my own and other children from poison such as arsenic. I regard it in that light."

(Letchworth Citizen ,16th September 1961)

Non-violent resistance and civil disobedience were well established means of protest available to normal citizens that, in the 20th Century, were most famously employed at the behest of Mahatma Gandhi in the struggle for Indian independence. It was his salt marches in the 1930s and other protests and strikes which forced politicians to the negotiating tables. Historically (and in modern times) these have not been without violent confrontation when oppressors endeavoured to suppress any opposition to their regimes, as happened in Amritsar in April 1919 when British officers commanded their troops to fire on a peaceful mass demonstration killing an estimated (but disputed by the British government) 1000 people. The subsequent cover up of the details of the event led to the Non Cooperation Movement in India.

Gandhi's struggle was not just for independence, but for social reform, and greater rural development. One of his most devoted followers was Mirabehn, who, after Gandhi's assassination in 1948, continued his campaign for rural and social reforms. She had a deep interest in organic husbandry and was a regular reader of *The Farmer* and the writings of Sir Albert Howard. According to Dr Bidisha Mallik, who made a detailed study of Mirabehn's life and work, 'impressed with the animal husbandry experiments of Newman Turner at his Goosgreen Farm in the Chilton Polden Hills of Somerset, Mirabehn desired to integrate some of Newman Turner's cattle breeding ideas into her scheme for the mountain people'. (Mallik, 2014, personal communication)

The Indian Government was set on using larger high milk yielding herds of cattle in the mountain regions, but these cattle were not suited to the higher altitude climate and terrain. Mirabehn, actively sought Frank's advice and help through correspondence in the mid-1950s, and brought his suggestions to the attention of the Prime Minister of India at that time, Jawaharlal Nehru. She had hoped to invite Frank out to her farm in Kashmir, and to import some Jerseys from his herd. Her plan to establish smaller shorter legged breeds, which might be more suited to the mountain conditions, were thwarted by the Indian government's refusal to fund such a scheme, and their determination to rely on indigenous breeds. It was not until Mirabehn returned to England in 1959, that Frank and Lorna were able to meet with her briefly at Friends' House, the Quaker headquarters in London.

****

Mirabehn (1892-1982)

Madeleine Slade was the daughter of Rear Admiral Sir Edmund Slade. She was an enthusiast of the music of Ludwig van Beethoven, and in pursuit of this interest came across a biography of Mahatma Gandhi. Inspired by his work, she wrote to ask if she might go to his Sahamarti Ashram. Gandhi invited her, and she set about training herself for the demands of the ascetic life in the Ashram that he had warned her would be necessary.

She arrived in India in 1925, and remained there for almost 35 years during which she accompanied Gandhi (who had given her the name Mirabehn after a devotee of The Lord Krishna) to round table conferences in London in 1931, and other events leading to India's independence. She was also imprisoned for her involvement in the Non Co-operation

Movement. After independence, she became active in dairying and farming in the foothills of the Himalayas before returning to England in 1959. In 1960, she moved to Austria to pursue her interest in Beethoven and she wrote a biography, The Spirit of Beethoven, which was published many years later as *Beethoven's Mystical Vision* (Khadi Friends Forum,1999). She died there in 1982.

****

Frank's friendship with Lawrence Hills served him well when he decided to launch *The Gardener* as a separate monthly magazine. By the mid-1950s, *The Farmer* had already had an organic gardening section added to it, and the first edition of *The Gardener – small livestock and pet owner* appeared in July 1957 with the strap line 'Edited by F Newman Turner from his farm, Associate Editor W E Shewell Cooper from his gardens, and Assistant Editor Lawrence D Hills'. In his first editorial (entitled 'At the Garden Gate', as a corollary to his editorials in *The Farmer*) Frank reiterated the mission statement he had published in the first edition of *The Farmer* in 1946. *The Gardener was published as a supplement to The Farmer. Now that we are issuing it as a separate monthly, the same principles, to the very last letter, apply with even more urgency to our new magazine, The Gardener. But whereas farmers concerned with economic survival are slow to be convinced of these new organic principles, gardeners, who are themselves the consumers of their own crops, must recognise at once the vital importance to the health of the family, of growing as much as possible of their daily diet by organic methods in the garden.*

There was a growing enthusiasm for organic approaches in the domestic horticulture world for which there had been no dedicated periodical in the UK. Shewell Cooper was a well-known gardening writer, who provided a diary feature from his horticulture centre near Thaxted in Essex, and Lawrence wrote about alpines for summer and autumn. Frank also commissioned a series on 'How to Train your Dog' by Barbara Woodhouse, based on her popular series of TV programmes. (Her stentorian command of 'Sit!' became a catchword for dog discipline throughout the land). Frank also contributed a series on 'Curing the Incurable Dog'. (Amongst his papers there is a manuscript for a book entitled Cure Your Own Dogs, written as a thesis for a doctorate of the National Institute of Medical Herbalists, but, as there was no one with the expertise to review it, it was never published.)

As Frank became more involved in clinical work as a consulting medical herbalist, another strand of his publishing enterprises opened. The National Institute of Medical Herbalists published a monthly magazine *Health from Herbs* which had been published since the foundation of the Institute in 1864. It had been edited for many years by Tom Bartram, a medical herbalist based in Bournemouth, who in his farewell editorial conveyed to all readers his best wishes 'with the sincere hope that bad health will follow them all their lives – and never catch them up! 'In Frank's first editorial for the October 1957 edition of *Health from Herbs* he wrote: *Living from the day I was born on and by the land; working all my life with soil, plants, and animals, watching things grow and learning from the example of creatures more innocent than man how and why each plant that grows in the earth can serve the life which moves over the earth; relating to the results of practical observation of the farm and checking them against the empirical knowledge recorded by the great botanists, herbalists, and nutritionists of the past, I have gained the unshakable conviction that health and physical well-being are the automatic consequences of the practice of natural law.*

Frank with Lorna at NIMH Centenary Conference, 1964

With the diversification of his editorial and publishing commitments, it seemed that *The Farmer* had served its purpose, and the last edition appeared in autumn 1957. But, Frank decided to widen the appeal of *Health from Herbs* by naming it *Fitness and Health from Herbs* which was launched in July 1958.

Like *The Gardener*, it was published in a pocket-sized format, and was priced at 1/6d or £1 for a year's subscription post free. Tom Bartram remained an Advisory Editor, joined by Frank Roberts, an eminent medical herbalist who practised in Bristol, and Doris Grant, who continued, as she had for *The Farmer,* to provide contributions on various aspects of healthy food and beauty. The broadcaster Michael Jackson, the *Fitness* sports editor, contributed features on 'Fitness Secrets of the Stars', including the boxer Freddie Mills, former light heavyweight champion of the world, Eamon Andrews, the TV presenter, and the singer, Eve Boswell. Another long serving writer for *The Farmer*, Dr Cyril Pink, continued to provide articles on natural childbirth while there were many contributions from leading medical herbalists such as W Burns Lingard. Albert Orbell, Louise Morley and Tom Bartram. All the articles were between two and four pages, short and easily readable.

Perhaps, the distractions of settling in to a new life in Letchworth may explain why the momentum of the publications began to wane a little. The May to September 1959 issue of *Fitness and Health from Herbs* was a slimmed down edition, partly enforced by a printing strike. Subsequently, a few editions were condensed by two months into one, yet mostly Frank managed to sustain the monthly magazine running to over 80 pages. But something had to give. Frank's editorial in the October 1960 edition of *The Gardener* announced the following: *The Gardener began its life as a supplement of The Farmer which I founded in 1945 for the purpose of advocating a complete system of organic nutrition through the proper growing of food on the farm and the garden. I believed that only by organic farming and gardening could we ensure the ultimate good health of the consumer. I was convinced that the farmer is the first important link in the chain of human health and that the organic growing of our food is essential to the building and maintenance of human health. To propagate home production of organic food by every health conscious householder we then published The Gardener as a separate monthly magazine. To complete our efforts to offer literature on organic health and nutrition I was happy to assume the editorship of Health from Herbs and give it a more comprehensive title of Fitness. The separate publication of these three magazines has proved after long and vigorous effort, to be quite impractical, both in available time to do it properly and above all economically. Further, few people have the time or money for so many separate magazines each contributing only a portion of the complete health programme. And, keen as I have been to maintain a separate magazine devoted entirely to organic gardening, advertisers have not supported us well enough even remotely to approach a revenue sufficient to cover the cost of publishing. So, the time seems right to unify our efforts in one comprehensive magazine combining the whole story of organic nutrition and medicine.*

******

Hydrogen Bomb Tests

The USA first tested an H Bomb in November 1952 at the Marshall Islands, in the Pacific Ocean. It was 100 times more powerful than the atomic bomb dropped on Hiroshima and destroyed an entire atoll. UK's first successful H-Bomb test was carried out at Malden Island in May 1957.

Lawrence D Hills
(1911–1990)

Lawrence D Hills was a well-known horticultural journalist and expert on alpine plants. He was the gardening correspondent of *The Observer* for eight years and also wrote regularly for the magazines *Punch* and *The Countryman* as well as for Frank's magazines, *The Farmer* and *The Gardener*. As a reader for Faber & Faber, he also assisted in the publication of Frank's books published by them in the early 1950s.

Lawrences particular enthusiasm was Russian Comfrey, which he believed to have great nutritional potential (and which Frank had later ascertained to be a source of vitamin B12). He developed a strain of comfrey which he named Bocking14 (as his nursery was based at Bocking near Braintree, in the county of Essex) and, through the medium of *The Farmer*, initiated 'The Great Comfrey Race' which encouraged growers worldwide to compete for the highest yields.

Russian Comfrey had been introduced in the nineteenth century by a Quaker smallholder named Henry Doubleday and, in 1954, Lawrence founded the Henry Doubleday Research Association (HDRA), to investigate the benefits of comfrey and promote organic horticulture in general, inviting Frank to become its first president, which he remained until his death ten years later. Now Garden Organic, HDRA is the world's largest organic gardening organisation.

Chapter 15

Rural Life to Radical Town

For a family who had lived in the countryside for the best part of twenty years, the transition to an urban existence was a big step to take, but Letchworth Garden City was no ordinary town. It had a reputation as a 'crank' town for the people it attracted rather than the ideology that lay behind its planning and foundation. Frank had been branded a crank often enough, so perhaps it had a certain appeal to him as a centre for radical ideas.

Letchworth is the world's First Garden City, founded in 1903, and inspired by the revolutionary ideas on town planning of Sir Ebenezer Howard. Howard (no known relationship to Sir Albert) was a parliamentary reporter who had written a book called Garden Cities of Tomorrow, a peaceful path to real reform (1898) in which he stated:

'Town and country must be married and out of their joyous union will spring a new hope, a new life, a new civilisation.'

He conceived the idea of The Three Magnets, the first two representing towns and the country with their respective drawbacks. The third magnet represented the bringing together of town and country to create an amalgam, that would resolve the decline of agriculture and rural life that was caused by the mass migration to cities and the consequent overcrowding and slums of urban conurbations in the Victorian era. Letchworth Garden City would have abundant green spaces and parks and residential streets well away from the industrial areas. The houses were mostly individually designed with adequate garden space for the residents to grow their own produce if they so wished.

The ethos of the town's founders made it attractive to a diverse range of religious groups, and radical and reform minded people. Early in the town's history, a Liberal Catholic Church was built and the Theosophical Society established a small branch with its own hall near the town centre. The Quaker Meeting House, Howgills, was built a little further to the south. A thriving Esperanto group was formed and, at a summer school held in 1912, a leading theosophist, Annie Besant, gave a talk on 'The Citizenship of Coloured Races,' a topic that still causes concern over 100 years later.

A thriving vegetarian society, formed in 1950 from an earlier health reform society, featured as speakers, the renowned vegetarian nature cure brothers Doctors Douglas and Gordon Latto, and Frank and Lorna's old friend and contributor to *The Farmer* and *Fitness*, Dr Cyril Pink. The introduction to an exhibition in 2017 exploring Letchworth's radical past stated: *Revolutions were discussed quietly and peacefully in people's homes while dining on vegetarian wholefoods. Its residents did not riot in the streets but paraded down them in medieval costume.*

Having sold the pedigree Jersey herd and farm implements by auction at Ferne, on August 30th 1958, our family moved to Letchworth. Frank and Lorna acquired a house, Deanrow, in Garth Road on the south side of the town, with a sizeable garden on a 1½ acre plot providing space for growing vegetables, fruit trees, a neglected tennis court and a small outdoor swimming pool which had become home to a community of frogs. The house had ample accommodation with a study for Frank which served as consulting room and a butler's pantry which made an ideal dispensary for his stock of herbal extracts. There were two garages, a double and a single, which they were able to convert to an office for the publications. Above the garage was an annex, which provided a small flat for RaeThompson. A further advantage of the location was its proximity to St Christopher School, a progressive, vegetarian, co-educational school which Giles and Adam could attend as day pupils.

Although effectively a town house, Frank was determined to maintain his country connections. Prior to moving to Letchworth, he arranged to take tenancy of a 1 ¼-acre plot behind a neighbouring house, which included an access strip beyond the boundary of Deanrow. Responding to a letter, from the surveyor of the First Garden City Ltd, confirming the offer of a tenancy, Frank wrote: *I note that "the land is to be used solely for the purpose of grazing horses" but assume that this phrase also covers cows or heifers or poultry, as we wish to use it for poultry and a house cow or two. As these are likely to be even less obtrusive than horses, I presume there will be no objection.*

The surveyor replied promptly to say that, they could not agree to the keeping of any livestock other than horses. So much for Howard's Third Magnet bringing town and country together!

Giles and Adam were enrolled as day pupils at St Christopher School and, having just left boarding school, I assisted in the publications office before enrolling at the British College of Naturopathy and Osteopathy in north London the following year. Frank established his practice as a consulting medical herbalist, and soon gained a following locally whilst commuting twice weekly to Bruton Street in London as the consultant of the Society of Herbalists, founded by Mrs C F Leyel in conjunction with her Culpeper Shops. Frank also continued to consult in Oxford and Harrogate on a monthly basis.

In order to serve his patients' needs more fully, Frank studied osteopathic techniques and, using his extensive knowledge and experience in the natural treatment of animals, sat the external examinations of the British Naturopathic and Osteopathic Association to obtain his Naturopathic Diploma (ND). He was also among the first practitioners in the UK to study acupuncture in the early 1960s, at a series of post-graduate lectures given by Dr Paul Geny and Dr Jacques Lavier, two French doctors who had studied in the Far East.

The magazines continued to present a challenge both in terms of their production against deadlines and, more critically, financially. Simmering in the background were the ongoing difficulties, with Herb Royal and Hans Lederman but he and Hans did take a business trip together to Germany the highlights of which he recorded on his 16mm cine camera.

His wide range of contacts in the herbal and naturopathic professions was a ready source of contributors, just as his agricultural connections had been when publishing *The Farmer*. He was a persuasive editor. At a time when any advertising by practitioners was restricted to an announcement of name, qualifications, and address in the listings at the back of the health magazines, he convinced his colleagues of the publicity exposure their contributions would give them for the very modest, or any fees he could afford to pay them. Frank's efforts in widening the readership of *Fitness and Health from Herbs* were rewarded with a Fellowship of the National Institute of Medical Herbalists in 1961.

Acupuncture in the UK

Prior to the late 1950s, acupuncture was practised in the UK by only a handful of doctors, who had studied it in Europe or Taiwan before mainland China became more accessible. Based on rather arcane rules and beliefs and defying any known anatomical basis, it did not sit comfortably with the analytical viewpoint of many conventional doctors. The concept of restoring balance through an adjustment of body energies, was more in harmony with the philosophy of naturopathic and herbal medicine and practitioners in these fields along with many physiotherapists and osteopaths soon became aware of the potential of acupuncture and moxibustion to alleviate pain, and help to remedy a wide range of acute and chronic disorders.

The first post-graduate teaching of osteopaths, naturopaths and physiotherapists was held in 1960 and '61 under the tuition of Dr Paul Geny and Dr Jacques Lavier, French doctors who had studied in Taiwan.

****

Frank seemed tireless in his pursuit of knowledge, both for his patients' benefit and for the readers of *Fitness* and *The Gardener*. In 1961, he joined a delegation of practitioners who visited one of the worlds' leading manufacturers of herbal and homoeopathic medicines, Dr Madaus in Cologne, Germany. Madaus had a research institute, and grew many of their botanic requirements organically. They also produced a large range of homoeopathic complex remedies, the oligoplexes, which could be prescribed on the basis of individual patient characteristics as well as their presenting symptoms.

Following their visit to Cologne the delegation visited the Ringberg Klinic in Bavaria where Dr Joseph Issels was providing innovative treatment for cancer patients based on naturopathic principles. Issels, like many innovators – some would call them mavericks – was controversial. At his clinic in Rottach Egern near Munich, he was employing biological treatments and dietary methods with some success and some failures in the management of cancer and these met with strong disapproval by his orthodox colleagues. He was arrested and faced trial for negligence and manslaughter for failing to recommend the conventional treatment at that time (predominantly radiation and chemotherapy) and his clinic was shut down. Frank featured the Issels controversy in *Fitness*. In his editor's Fitness Forum in the July/August 1961 edition he wrote: *It was clear to me after a long talk with Dr Issels that the innocence or guilt of the man in   the   dock (and Dr Issels, the dedicated healer that I had known him to be will not mind this perspective) is only of secondary importance compared with the decision which the court findings are bound to make as to whether biological methods of cancer treatment are to be allowed by the medical authorities in Germany (and in consequence in other countries) when all orthodox methods have failed ...Dr Issels is, therefore, fighting not so much to free himself from the threat of gaol and ruin, but to free natural healers from the restrictions which prevent them from offering their knowledge and experience to sufferers from cancer and other proscribed diseases.*

Over fifty years later, the debates still rage between those who seek to suppress innovative natural treatments – upholding the entrenched views of some scientists in the guise of protecting the public from charlatans – and those who recognise the need to embrace new ideas and put them to the test. The history of medical science abounds with ideas whose originators have faced ostracism and scorn only later to be found of therapeutic merit. After a four year legal battle all charges against Dr Issels were overturned and the Ringberg Klinic was re-licensed.

The herbal tradition dates back many hundreds of years in the UK (King Henry V111 granted a Royal Charter to medical herbalists in the 16th century) but natural medicines are more widely used and accepted in Europe. Evidence of this lies in the success of many manufacturers of herbal and homoeopathic remedies, especially in Germany and Switzerland where firms such as Madaus, Wala, Weleda, and Bioforce are all well established and often have their own research facilities. As demand for these products by English herbalists and naturopaths developed, two of them, Sidney Rose Neil and Kenneth Basham, set up a small import company called Biomed Associates to supply practitioners with a range of the Madaus company's medicines manufactured in Cologne. The Madaus Company was founded in 1919 by the three sons of Frau Magdalena Madaus, a heilpraktiker (the German equivalent of a naturopath) to

211

manufacture her formulations. These complexes of herbal and homoeopathic remedies were prescribed according to traditional indications and constitutional characteristics of the patient. Complexes and traditional medicines of this nature are popular in Germany and became widely used throughout Europe.

Frank, like many medical herbalists, made up his patients' prescriptions from fluid extracts and tinctures which he was able to obtain from old established UK firms such as Potters and Carters but also, conveniently, from William Ransom & Sons in neighbouring Hitchin, who manufactured the herbal extracts sold by many of the other companies. The Madaus oligoplex, complex remedies were convenient to prescribe and were helpful to patients with a wide range of acute and chronic illnesses. Madaus also manufactured other innovative medicines which were imported by Biomed Associates. But in late 1963, the line of supply was under threat when the lady who ran Biomed for Basham and Rose Neil had to give it up because of poor health. So, Frank decided that he and Lorna would take on the agency. It would be a useful little sideline for Lorna, he believed!

A corner of the garage of Deanrow was found for the extensive range of oligoplexes, and other products. Having recently graduated as a naturopath and osteopath, I was put to work packing and invoicing the products ordered by practitioners, between acting as a locum for Frank's osteopathic patients when he was away. Soon it became necessary to rent warehouse accommodation in the town, as they also took on the agency for Swiss health food products which had previously been imported by Culpeper House. Bio Strath was, a herbal elixir produced by a process of fermenting yeasts with honey and plant extracts; Biotta was a range of vegetable juices which had been subjected to a lacto fermentation process rendering them more digestible and enhancing their health benefits. They also introduced a caffeine free cereal beverage based on barley, figs, and chicory, called Pionier. These products together with the Madaus medicines were then marketed under a new limited company, Intermedics which incorporated Biomed Associates.

Having added osteopathic skills to his therapeutic armamentarium Frank, made use of it for his London patients, when indicated, but the Society of Herbalists, objected to him using this on patients, who were attending what was primarily supposed to be an herbal practice. Like many naturopaths, Frank preferred to integrate treatments such as osteopathy, acupuncture, herbal, and nutritional medicine to provide the best possible outcomes for his patients. In a situation that seemed to be echoing the objections of Miss Lind af Hagaby to his running the publications from Ferne Farm, he was being asked not to muddle their message. But, within the bounds of nature's laws, Frank was an eclectic, so he decided to take rooms in Welbeck Street, close to Harley Street in the heart of London's West End, where he could be free to practise as he wished.

Eclecticism in practice was all very well but was his diversity of business interests spreading his financial, physical, and emotional resources too thinly? Their mini empire now comprised the practices, the publications, Intermedics, and Herb Royal. All were under capitalised – this much is clear from the red print in the balance columns of the bank statements – but so, too, were Frank's own health resources. Introducing a special feature on preventing heart attack in the January 1963 edition of *Fitness*, Frank wrote in his editorial of the importance of a comprehensive approach to cardiovascular health. *To eat wholefood as nearly as possible as it is naturally grown, manipulated only to the extent that is required to wash and cut up but not to boil and bake is the ideal. Subject to some preparatory emptying (by fasting) and restoring (by dietary and herbal treatment) impaired digestive and eliminative organs, such a diet will produce the best results in any state of disease or health.*

But even assuming the perfect diet the greatest need of all for the heart is physical activity. The heart must work to be enabled to continue to work.

There was a time when I thought I was running into trouble with my heart. But I soon found the trouble was that I wasn't running (or walking) enough. I wasn't aware of the fact, till I sought some life insurance and found that my blood pressure was too high for the insurance company.

I was too busy at the time to do much about it and in fact the amount of exercise I took, became less and less. I put on weight until I was 217lbs which for my height of 5ft 11inches was far too much. It became too much for comfort as well as for health, so I did determine to lose weight and at the same time benefit my health and I hope, my blood pressure.

I went on an all raw diet for one month, commencing with a short fast, and three days on fresh fruit only. I lost 28lbs of weight in 30 days and felt fine. But my blood pressure was not permanently reduced though it was much improved. Another year or so passed but still I was above insurable (at normal rates) blood pressure. By now I was feeling chest pains which were unmistakable signs of angina of effort. All my dieting

214

had been of little avail apart from a beneficial loss of weight. Still, I was too busy, or too lazy, to take much exercise. I tried instead a prolonged course of herbal medicine and both blood pressure and chest pains improved, but did not return to normal.

It was obvious that from a former life of great physical activity I had got to the stage of life when my brain was greatly employed, but my muscles were semi-retired. I was extending my brain to the utmost but never my heart and arteries. Instead I was rapidly extending (or distending) my abdomen again.

I was brought up on my father's farm and had a farm myself for some twenty years. This gave me early years of much physical effort. During my university years I maintained this hard physical activity by playing rugby football twice a week and boxing at the gymnasium and for my university an average of twice a week. For additional training, I played squash and fives. I continued leaving university to play rugger and do farm work whenever possible.

But as my healing work and writing increased my physical activities decreased. So, it seems my muscles became increasingly lined with deposits of fat – for my enjoyment of food did not decrease. This is the fate of many middle aged men who are very active in youth. The heart is a mass of muscle and, like all the other muscles of the body, if is not expanded to its full capacity regularly, preferably daily, it acquires layers of fat which increasingly limits its ability to expand.

Walking was the first and easiest activity; a deliberate dose of straightforward time for walking there and back. Boring of course but so is most medicine and at least it didn't taste too bad, to breathe deeply fresh air again with having to do those ridiculous breathing exercises in front of an open window. Then I took up squash rackets again when I felt fit for such a fast strenuous game. I would not recommend suspected heart patients to start playing squash except after prolonged and progressive training or without first consulting a practitioner. I played for about an hour a week in addition to walking and felt great exhilaration shortly after each game. After the first few days increased effort I had no further chest pains.

My blood pressure steadily reduced. Most surprising of all to me I found, once in training, that my blood pressure was lower after a game of squash than for some days before. The expansion of the heart muscles to their fullest elasticity widened the passages of the associated blood vessels. ... I am confident that this regime will have delayed my final heart attack.

His confidence was, perhaps, misplaced. Despite this advice and his experience of the benefits of exercise, in the late summer of 1963 Frank suffered a mild heart attack. Luckily enough, from his point of view, he did not have to be hospitalised. (In retrospect, it might have been better if he had been and the state of his coronary arteries had been monitored, although, at that time, the present day sophistication of acute cardiac management was only in its infancy.) He made modest concessions to the need for rest but was not entirely shielded from the ongoing stresses of Herb Royal, the challenges of the publication deadlines for the magazine, and helping Lorna with getting Intermedics launched. I can recall him sitting in the lounge at Deanrow correcting galley proofs (rather as he had done on cliff tops at Godrevy during family holidays.) Because of his blood pressure problems, he continued to curtail his intake of animal fat which, as a lacto vegetarian meant, avoiding butter and cheese, and he started using olive oil on his morning toast. But he admitted that the foundations of his arterial damage might have been laid in his youth on the family farm and later consuming the milk of his high butterfat yielding Jersey cows. Nevertheless, after a short period of rest, he also returned to his graded exercise programme.

With the loyal assistance of Rae Thompson and a part time typist in the office he kept the monthly publication of *Fitness* more or less on schedule and contributed a number of the articles. He attended the Centenary Conference of the National Institute of Medical Herbalists, held at the Guildhall, London in March 1964, and reported on it in the May edition of *Fitness*. He was getting back to a full time routine with both practice and publishing, punctuated by the problematic relationship with Hans Lederman and matters in Bridgwater. Hans was seeking a merger of Herb Royal with a larger pet food manufacturer, and Frank and Lorna were not happy with this further threat to their control of the company. In early June, Hans had prepared a report setting out what he described as the 'precarious financial situation after poor trading in 1963 and early 1964', and putting a strong case for introducing more capital by a merger of Herb Royal with a larger company. This weighed heavily on their minds and on Frank's chest. But their silver wedding anniversary was approaching, and it was time to take a holiday of sorts.

They couldn't get away on their anniversary date, June 3rd, as Frank had to put to bed the July 1964, edition of *Fitness* but once that had been done and arrangements were in place for me to act as locum and treat those of his patients needing osteopathic care, they were able to set off for Switzerland, and Germany with Adam. The plan was to visit several suppliers of products in Switzerland and then return through Germany calling on Willy Schlüter Kg in Bingen and Madaus in Cologne. It was not exactly a complete diversion from the pressures of business. They had an enjoyable few days around Lake Zurich trying to keep the somewhat bored thirteen year old Adam amused, and then travelled up to Bingen on Rhine.

It was on the morning of Sunday, the 28th June, that I received a telephone call at Deanrow from Herr Freund, the export manager of Madaus, who put Lorna on the line. She told me that Dad had died. My first thought was that he had had an accident but she explained that he had woken early that morning complaining of pains in his chest and arms and had then had a seizure as his heart stopped. He was fifty.

Herr Freund had driven down from Cologne to assist, being fluent in English (which the Schlüter people in Bingen were not). He told me that Frank's body would have to be sealed in a zinc lined coffin to comply with customs regulations before being sent home by road. I told Giles, who had just arrived home after being away overnight, and then walked to the top of the garden, where Rae was pursuing her favourite pastime, and broke the news to her. She simply said "Oh!" and carried on weeding as I left her to her own thoughts and walked back to the house to break the news to other members of the family including the Clarks in Cornwall and Frank's mother, sister, and brothers in Yorkshire. The following day I drove into London, saw a few patients at the rooms in Welbeck Street, then went to the airport to meet

Lorna and Adam, who flew back from Cologne. A couple of days later the coffin arrived in a large hearse and was placed in Frank's study at Deanrow.

The funeral was held at the Quaker Meeting House, Howgills, in Letchworth but the zinc lined coffin and Frank's 15 stone bulk were too heavy for us brothers to carry in the usual manner, and we had to wheel him in on a trolley. He was interred at Letchworth municipal cemetery on a plot set aside for Quaker burials. Lorna could never bring herself to arrange for a gravestone, even the simplest Quaker memorial, and we didn't wish to raise the topic and evoke the painful memories that never really left her.

Some years later, after Lorna had died, we planted a London Plane tree in his memory at Ryton near Coventry, the headquarters of Garden Organic (formerly HDRA), of which he had been the first president until his death. Frank had always jokingly said that when he went, his body should be thrown on the compost heap. It was a sad irony that his wish to return to the soil was thwarted by the bureaucracy of national boundaries.

Epilogue

Frank Newman Turner left unfinished business. It is impossible to know how much more he would have achieved if he had lived out even a normal lifespan. Looked at from the perspective of over sixty years later, it is certain that the radical ideas he expressed in his articles, lectures, books, and publications have gained some respectability. But have the ideals propagated by him and his contemporaries in the organic farming, health reform, or peace movements brought about any lasting change in the world?

There has been a tremendous growth in the demand and supply of organic produce, but there is still an enormous divide between industrialised agribusiness and true agriculture – the nurturing of nature's wisdom in farming and gardening. There is increased demand for the integration of patient-centred healthcare with the technological advances of modern medicine, which Frank would surely have welcomed. But there is still a culture of disease confrontation and subjugation of nature, driven by the mega-million financial demands of the pharmaceutical industry and overwhelming the principles of health creation that underpin the natural therapeutic professions. And the lessons of the past seem to be ignored by an increasingly divided, nationalistic world prone to conflicts, which generate aggression, rather than seeking a path to peaceful resolution.

I feel sure Frank would have been heartened by the growing recognition of our essential synergy with the natural world, while continuing his measured approach to raising awareness of its importance to our lives. Not for him the messianic rhetoric and tub-thumping dogmatism of some campaigners. He always remembered the wise words of Sir Albert Howard to him, when he was a young man: "We cannot hope to win the masses; we must go forward with the enlightened minority."

Walking the farm with students at Goosegreen, circa 1950. Note the tripods in the background.
(Photo: Douglas Allen)

Clearly, he was driven to make people more aware of the relationship of the soil to the health of plants, animals, and mankind but there were other pleasures in life. Frank's diaries from the 1930s, documented the concerts, theatres, and sporting events he attended. The move to Somerset and the demands of the farms, curtailed these diversions for Frank and Lorna, apart from occasional outings to take Giles and me to a pantomime at the Bristol Hippodrome or to the Somerset county cricket ground at Taunton. There was also their small collection of 78 rpm records acquired in the 1930s and 1940s, including the Mills Brothers and an ornately decorated twelve inch record of Paul Whiteman's Orchestra at the Biltmore, featuring Sophie Tucker and Bing Crosby (one of his favourites) singing in his first professional engagement as one of The Rhythm Boys. There was a recording of the Harry Lime theme, played on the zither by Anton Karas, in the film The Third Man, and there were records of music by Chopin, Tchaikovsky, and Ivor Novello (whose stage performances they had enjoyed). These were all played from time to time on the Philco radiogram in the sitting room at Goosegreen. They also had a pianola, and a collection of piano rolls which sat for many years in a box in the attic at Goosegreen. (The pianola disappeared after our move to Ferne Farm and we never did ascertain what became of it.)

Such moments, however, could only be transitory for a farmer with cows to milk, fields to cultivate, and crops to harvest; they could only be tasted in small bites for a writer and publisher with deadlines to be met; they could only be a rare pleasure for a practitioner with the needs of his patients to prioritise; they could only be a diversion to anticipate the fuller indulgence of when time permitted. It seldom did. But then, as my brothers have pointed out, his work was also his hobby.

His determination to expand upon the principles, set out by others before him, and his commitment to demonstrate the wisdom of working with nature drove him on. The practical measures he described in his books are still relevant today, and they have become classics of the organic movement, which remain in print in new editions published by Acres USA, one of the leading eco-agriculture organisations in North America. There can be no doubt that the efforts of Frank and his contemporaries laid the foundations for the growing ranks of 'the enlightened minority' in the 21st century.

The legacy, which would have given him the most satisfaction, however, would be his own family who have endeavoured to carry forward and live by the precepts he held dear – peaceful co-existence, respect for the supremacy of nature, and compassion for all living things.

An Agricultural Glossary

Curry comb – Hand-tool with short rubber teeth for grooming cattle or horses

Hay tedder – Horse- or tractor-drawn machine with rotating tines to scatter new-mown hay to improve drying.

Lades – Boards fitted to the sides of a cart to give it greater capacity.

Ley – Temporary pasture sown with mixed herbs for grazing.

Pollarding – Cutting back branches of trees, especially willows, to form a close head.

Priest hole – Concealed hiding place in old houses for catholic priests who were persecuted in the 16th century.

Rhines (pronounced as reens) – Drainage ditches between fields in low-lying land.

Frank Newman Turner –
A Chronology

1913 Born into Yorkshire farming family, near Barnsley. Eldest of five children.

1924-1934 Education Barnsley Grammar School and Leeds University – National Diploma in Agriculture, National Diploma in Dairying.

1930s Worked for Potato Marketing Board in London. Wrote regular features for *Farmer's Weekly*, *Farmer & Stockbreeder* and other agricultural publications.

Attended Peace Pledge Union meetings – addressed by Dick Sheppard and others. Registered as Conscientious Objector. Became a member of Society of Friends (Quakers).

1939 Married Lorna Clark, June 3rd, daughter of the manager of Farm Industries for West Cornwall. Lived at White Cottage, nr Barnet.

1940 Son, Roger, born at Radlett. Moved to Goosegreen Farm near Bridgwater, Somerset, to manage farm for training COs to work on the land.

1940s Began the organic experiment inspired by Sir Albert Howard. After the war bought the farm and developed ideas of organic husbandry and natural treatment of animals.

1945 Son, Giles, born at Stonefield Maternity home in Wookey Hole, Somerset (Evacuated from Blackheath and run by Dr Cyril Pink).

1946 Founded The Farmer magazine 'edited and published from *the farm*.'

1946 – 1953 Weekend courses held at Goosegreen – on composting, herbal leys, self-feed silage, animal husbandry, no-ploughing cultivation, etc. Attended by followers of organic methods from all walks of life.

1949 Set up Organic Herbal Products in nearby Bridgwater, Somerset to produce herbal veterinary products and pet foods.

1950 Son, Adam, born at Stonefield Maternity Home in Blackheath.

1950 Cure your Own Cattle published by The Farmer Publications.

1951 *Fertility Farming* published by Faber & Faber.

1953 Moved from Goosegreen Farm to Ferne estate near Shaftesbury, Dorset. *Herdsmanship* published by Faber & Faber.

1955 *Fertility Pastures* published by Faber & Faber.

1956 *The Farmer* 10th Birthday Luncheon held at the De Vere Hotel, Kensington. FNT qualified as medical herbalist and became consultant for the Society of Herbalists in London and Harrogate.

1957 Last edition of *The Farmer*. Newman Turner Publications continued to publish *The Gardener and Fitness and Health from Herbs* (magazine of the National Institute of Medical Herbalists of which he had become editor).

1958 Sold pedigree Jersey herd and farm tools. Moved to Letchworth Garden City, Hertfordshire and established practice as a medical herbalist, later embracing naturopathy, osteopathy, and acupuncture.

1962 Awarded Fellowship of National Institute of Medical Herbalists.

1962 Acquired Inter-Medics Ltd to preserve the agency and supply of the Madaus herbal medicines for practitioners. Expanded this to import Pionier, Schlüter baths, Biotta, Bio-Strath, and Biokosma.

1964 Died of coronary thrombosis in Bingen, Germany, whilst visiting suppliers of Inter-Medics products.

CPSIA information can be obtained
at www.ICGtesting.com
Printed in the USA
LVHW042034010323
740699LV00003B/457